Bahamian Anthology

College of the Bahamas

MACMILLAN
CARIBBEAN

Macmillan Education
Between Towns Road, Oxford OX4 3PP
A division of Macmillan Publishers Limited
Companies and representatives throughout the world

www.macmillan-caribbean.com

ISBN 0 333 34818 4

Text © College of Bahamas 1983

First published 1983

Printed in China

2005 2004 2003 2002 2001
13   12   11   10   9   8   7   6

Contents

1 Prose

2 Poetry

3 Plays

Acknowledgements

The compilers wish to thank the following people and organisations:
all writers for copyright of their materials;
Collins Publishers for 'Single Seven' from *Back Home*; Johnson's Publications for 'Ordeal at Sea' from *Ordeal at Sea and Other Stories*; Timpaul Company for 'Where Is It' from *Bain Town*; Star Publishing Co. for 'Psychologically Speaking' from *Psychologically Speaking* and for 'Political Farce' from *Refracted Thought*; House of Sesum for 'Mailboat to Hell', 'Power' and 'Breakfast Bruise' from *Reflections*; Dorrance and Co. for 'The March of the Hermit Crabs in the Rain' from *Voyage in the Sunset* and for 'Ole Zeke' and 'Islan' Life' from *Bahamian Scene*; Macmillan Education for 'Ode' and 'Encounter with a Chickcharney, from *Song of the Surreys* and for 'Crossing the Creek' and 'Bulla Claudy Funeral' from *Island Echoes*;
Rex Nettleford for the Foreword;
Dr Marcella Taylor for the Critical introduction, for the Writers' Workshop, for reviewing materials and suggesting editing;
Stan Burnside for the cover illustration;
I.B.M. for the donation of funds;
City Markets for the donation of funds;
Nassau Underwriters for the donation of funds;
Xerox Company for duplication of the manuscript;
the original committee – Robert Johnson, Keva Bethel, M. Kazim Bacchus, Susan Wallace, Roger Brown, Sean McWeeney, Winston Saunders, Daniel Duncombe – for initiating the activity and screening materials;
the second committee – Barry Hynes, Claire Belgrave, Marjorie Jones, Janyne Rahming, Mel Rahming, Verona Seymour, Arlene Ferguson, Haldane Chase, Ellen Serville – for final screening of material and other activities leading to publication, with very special thanks to Barry Hynes, co-ordinator, whose persistence, determination and tenacity made this anthology a reality;
the present committee – Claire Belgrave, Felicity Johnson, Celestine Cooper, Haldane Chase, Earl Cash, Margaret Thomas, Pearl Monaghan;
Earl Cash, for work on the study guide.

Foreword

An anthology of Bahamian creative writing follows naturally on the nation's conscious efforts over the past decade to reconstruct a new society and define its national identity. To a people emerging from institutionalised dependency and a prolonged impoverishment of that spirit associated with being integrated self-directed souls, the urge to celebrate the new won liberation in forms more lasting than the light-hearted minstrelsy of plantation and the colonial years is both desired and desirable. For creative writing, like the many other artistic products of the creative intellect and the creative imagination, remain the deepest record, the deepest impulse and the deepest resource of the human spirit.

That this should be made to serve the process of achieving not only the release of individual creative ability but also the collective *force vitale* of an entire society is clearly realised by the Bahamians who are responsible for promoting this first anthology of Bahamian literature.

It will no doubt add to the already growing corpus of literature that has long been coming out of the Caribbean and the wider Plantation America which are both the creature of one of the most dynamic and complex processes of human interaction and cultural cross-fertilisation over the past five hundred years. Out of the belly of the beast of colonisation and slavery and the consequences of dehumanisation and suffering have come the art of survival, the skills of struggle and manifestations of human courage. The celebration of much of this in an indigenous literature – with the lexicon of Europe, the tonal texture of Africa and the syntax and special pecularities of the Caribbean and the Americas – is a Bahamian acknowledgement of a rich heritage which challenges us all to exploration and to a creativity that bears the mark of revolutionary integrity.

But here the Bahamian writer will do well to heed the advice of a fellow-Caribbean writer – Jose Luis Mendez of Puerto Rico. 'In the same way that specialists in particular fields of endeavour demonstrate high quality and efficiency', he once said, 'the writer . . . must realise that literature is a form of action with its own laws, though not autonomous, employing specific techniques and particular tools which must be known, explored and improved. He must realise, too, that the best way to make literature serve a revolutionary cause is to regard it seriously as art . . .'

The building of a new Bahamian nation reflecting a civilised Bahamian society is a revolutionary cause. For the Bahamian writer to serve that cause he must regard his literature seriously as art – with a deep sense of caring and a dedication to excellence. This anthology is a beginning on the road, hopefully, to contributing to the determination of the mainstream of the literature of mankind. And out of the patrimony of a rich heritage and a vibrant, challenging contemporary life will always come the source of energy for this and more . . .

Rex Nettleford
Professor of Extra-Mural Studies
University of the West Indies, Mona, Jamaica.

Critical introduction

The appearance of a first anthology of imaginative works from an emerging culture makes one ask questions regarding the meaning of such an event. Such questions lead to other questions – questions about the function of literature and of art in general, questions about the significance of the presence or absence of artistic production in a culture and, finally, questions regarding the manner in which the particular group of writings now being published – as in this Bahamian collection – contribute to the enrichment of the culture that gave it birth and of other cultures. This essay suggests tentative answers to these questions.

Let me begin by setting forth a provisional definition of art: An art work is an imaginative structure created as an expression of what it means to be human; this aesthetic form functions primarily as an object of perception. Imaginative structures are numerous and may include anything that is not found in nature, e.g. a frying pan, a typewriter, a sculpture, a piece of music, a ball-point pen and a flowerpot. Therefore, the other two parts of the definition – an aesthetic form that expresses our humanness and that functions primarily as an object of perception – must more clearly separate the work of art from other artifacts.

If the object is intended primarily for perception, such items as the frying pan or the typewriter will be excluded; the definition will then include such objects as the piece of music or the sculpture. Although we may refer to the products of the craftsperson as a useful art, when I refer to 'art' here I mean those objects which appear to have no function except to be observed, enjoyed and appreciated, that is, such things as paintings, films, plays, stories and musical compositions.

But if these forms function only as objects of perception, then we may ask, of what *use* are they in human society? To examine that question properly, we need to explore in greater detail the manner in which they pattern human feelings and experience.

A work of art does not normally give us a photographic image of life. The artist uses the tools – oils, marble, words, etc. – to create a form that exists not in the order of nature (the given world) but in the order of the imagination. In doing so, the artist may use three types of material from life: 1) the sounds, colours, shapes, movements, etc. in the environment; 2) people, and events that actually occur; 3) the basic human feelings that the artist has come to understand and, perhaps, experience.

Of these three, the third is the central component. The stories, poems and plays in this anthology will in some way reflect the feelings the writers have come to know. These feelings will be most often feelings dominant in the society; further, one can most certainly assume that the feelings portrayed here are echoed in other peoples of the world, at many other points in human history.

In the development of the various cultures, works of art do not serve only to enhance; they are an integral part of the growth of a culture. We can make tremendous efforts to educate for progress in scientific and economic areas but this human world would probably end in technological cataclysm if values born of human sensitivities did not catalyse our dreams and direct our endeavours.

Thus societies need to educate the emotions as well as the intellect for, where our rational understanding falters, our intuitive awareness must be sharpened to carry us on. This unlocking of our intuitive faculties and of the emotional content of our lives is the function of the work of art. The expressive form takes over where the language of discourse fails.

Thus the human feeling portrayed in any work of art is at centre and, in one sense, what images of nature are replayed in the representational content of the work does not matter. A Bahamian writer constructing a story placed in Rome would be probably still imaging feelings that find echo among Bahamians for, even as we journey, it is rare that we can jettison our inheritance. Nevertheless, the selection of works for this particular anthology makes us focus on Bahamian characters in a Bahamian environment and these elements serve an additional function.

For if art takes from life, art also gives to life. The writer who uses the images of nature to inform the work being created is also giving back to nature an image of itself. Primitive cultures believed that only that part of the world made sacred by being represented in myth or ritual was *real*; the rest of the world was *profane* (secular) and thus never truly existed. Despite the fact that today we may embrace the earthliness of our existence, we can acknowledge that writers, like all artists, make their cultures real, give their societies a solid place in the magnificient panorama of history, a place that would either be lost or visible only in vague outlines without the artist. The world of nature is a world of fragmentation and chaos. History texts can present only partial truths. The artist frames a minute segment of the world, temporally as in music or story, spatially as in painting or sculpture, thereby giving human existence a form that brings a conclusion to the aimless shiftings and uncertainties of our lives. Once art has taught us that it is possible to perceive form and meaning by examining segments of our world, that world becomes less confusing.

Further, through its presentation of images of human feelings, works of

5

art help us to understand ourselves and others and the tensions and tentative resolutions that occur typically in human lives. These understandings would scarcely exist if we did not have literature or paintings or musical compositions to chart the conflicting shapes of human experience. Further, each of us would feel very alone with our inexpressible feelings if we were not constantly reminded by the products of the artistic imagination that we are not alone.

For all these reasons and more, we must greet an anthology such as this one with a sigh of relief for it is a sign that there are writers who have been struggling to present images of shared feelings and thus to make their world, their cultures, truly exist, now and always.

The place taken by such a culture, and such results of literary effort, is, however, not analogous to an oasis in a desert. Rather it is like a new tree in the forest. For cultures and literatures are interrelated, each receiving and then giving. Writers exist and flourish because of the writers who have left them an inheritance of literary forms and primordial symbols. These charge the contemporary writers to use the images and forms, to modify and develop them and to hand them on in their turn. Just as all cultures are part of one world that moves toward a destiny which none of us can know, all literatures become part of one totality that is Literature.

The major genres of literature are represented in this collection; prose essays and narratives, poems and plays. However, there are certain pieces which must be distinguished from the others in that, like folk literatures, they seem to be written out of familiar conventions.

Folk forms

Mizpah's Tertullien's *Cocoa Plumming* records an adventure of Brer Rabbie and Brer Bookie, favourite Bahamian folk characters, of whom many tales were once told. The story ends with a moral, typical of the tale told to children or to people in small communities who depend on such stories for moral and social guidance.

The messages in the *Smokey Joe Says* extracts as well as those in *Psychologically Speaking* move us into the social and political areas. All these authors have a statement to make that emerges clearly through the dramatic material. This is true even though, in the *Smokey Joe* selections at least, feeling and presentation are stronger than concept.

Smokey Joe, the character created by Eugene Dupuch, became a familiar 'visitor' to Bahamian households. When I was a child, everyone waited with anticipation for the newspaper edition that would carry another monologue of the beloved Smokey Joe with his witty and brilliant insights into the ways of 'folks,' even those folks who were civil servants or politicians, at home and abroad. I can recall how, on the arrival of the paper, my father would immediately open it at the column and read it aloud in a dialect and tone that perfectly matched the literary voice Dupuch had created. Smokey Joe was the Bahamian classic.

While, in *Psychologically Speaking*, Mizpah Tertullien directs her words to a society become more sophisticated, it nevertheless appears that she writes out of the tradition established in *Smokey Joe Says*.

While these pieces come to us as individual creations, we can ally them to folk forms for they assume that the material and the dramatic conventions are familiar to their audiences. The genre established allows each particular selection to refer back to the genre itself. But in *Smokey Joe Says*, Dupuch himself establishes the model and its conventions.

As we turn to the other prose selections and the plays, we find fewer obvious conventions working. Each piece appears to be a fresh invention. The material is both factual and fictional and it is no doubt true that in the 'factual' selections, the fictional intrudes because of the way a writer uses the imagination to remember and in the 'fictional' selections, factual experiences help to inform the presentation of characters and events.

The prose

The most 'factual' piece is Cleveland Eneas' *Where is it?* in which he describes a residential section of New Providence, Bain Town. Though on the surface an informative piece, vivid details ('the odours of baking bread,' the 'rock walls,' the 'lye barrel') draw the reader into the world evoked, making the experience of reading it an emotive one.

Similar in pattern is Ileana McDermott's *Market Street in the Thirties*, but here there is less concern with a full, detailed presentation and more with the associative memory process. Details of sponge merchants dominate because they are the dominant image of the writer's reverie. The feeling of nostalgia enters the narrative, a feeling that belongs not only to the writer but to each of us for things that have moved irrevocably into the past.

Eunice Humblestone's *Mr and Mrs Robinson* is also written out of the order of memory. In relaxed but vivid prose, she too brings figures out of a childhood past, making real for the reader Mr Robinson, 'the neighbourhood philosopher', and Mrs Robinson, who spent most of her time in a kitchen always black.

Melissa Maura's tale is not from childhood; the narrator is a young adult who adds to our gallery another unforgettable figure, Veronica. Here the narrator is effaced for Veronica occupies centre stage intriguing us, making us feel what her narrator-friend feels, the joy and wonder– and, perhaps, envy– that accompanies the encounter with the 'Veronicas' of the world. Yet *Veronica*, like the others, ends on a note of nostalgia, that yearning to reach back toward a cherished segment of our lives, which may or may not return some day. The less likely that return, the more poignant the evoked memory.

Like the other five pieces discussed here, A.C. Smith's *Dog* enacts a lost image as if in the hope of making it live again. An adult narrator remembers from childhood a neighbourhood character, a derelict. 'Dog' stays apart most of the time but demonstrates his own folk wisdom when he points to a child's ball to say, 'This is life. A circle. All goin' round and round and comin' back to the same spot.' There is here the conventional use of a circular object as symbol but such an image is reawakened as it is placed within the earthy context of this story. For Dog, too, has inherited his symbol-making capacity from stories and, when confronted with the ball, tries to pass on such meaning for the child. In response, he becomes the subject of community concern. The primary feeling in the work is portrayed as the community reaches out to nourish one of its members.

The endurance of memory and the sweet tyranny of nostalgia are elements of works that emerge out of the writer's reverie of the past. The story may be a form of ritual designed to make permanent in art what is passing in life: moments and encounters that are significant enough to be cherished.

All narrative, even fictional, occurs in the form of memory. There is always the pretence of events that occured 'once upon a time'. Chester Thompson's prose piece, *An Eye for an Eye*, falls into the pattern of the sea-mystery-crime adventure but combines such motifs with a revenge motif and an incident of poetic justice that brings the story to a denouement which leaves the reader satisfied but thoughtful.

In *Ordeal at Sea*, C. Tatem uses a song, a hymn sung as people wait out a storm praying that all those at sea will arrive home safely. But the story transcends its genre, the contest-with-nature tale, for it presents characters drawn individually as they battle not only with the waters but also with their personal pasts and their present choices. The story becomes starkly realistic as those who are strongest must allow those who are weakest to die. This is not a tale constructed easily from the mould of herioc sea tales but one written with a knowledge of the true contours of the sea and the human soul.

The prose selections then portray figures that emerge not only out of fictional knowledge of islands, small communities and the sea and its shores but out of firsthand knowledge of such, for the writers have grown up in landscapes similar to those which gave Greek, Norse and English literatures their beginnings.

If narrative looks to the past, drama looks to the future. Plays relate closely to the societies which give them birth; they are a vision of what the people and the civilisation will or could become. There is an element of daydream here but often the daydream must walk hand in hand with reality. For only through an encounter with reality is the future made significant.

Plays

Like Macbeth, Percival Miller's Potato Dreamer (*The Potato Dreamer*) must finally lay aside his dreams. But the play centres on those dreams, and as it balances between the real and the fanciful, we can see a figure of ourselves caught between 'that which we have' and 'that which we would have'.

A writer well-known for her ability to capture Bahamian voices and attitudes is Susan Wallace. She begins her play *Single Seven* with characterisations of a couple who, like many of their fellow Bahamians, are ready to read 'signs and portents' in the Scriptures and in dreams (or even in the waking world wherever numbers occur.) They then play these numbers in the numbers racket but, unfortunately, there are too many oracles and too many possible number combinations.

The play is highly skilful both in its portrayal of human situations and its manipulations of the various signs and passages from Scriptures. It keeps its humour all the way through to the denouement when a scriptural passage for the day, 'Beware of false prophets' comes true in an unexpected context.

The play is anti-myth for, rather than following a traditional dramatic pattern, it uses the pattern (an oracle which is a riddle that produces anguish) in order to overturn it. Thus, it is ironic rather than tragic, comic rather than pathetic. Further, the comic situation is heightened in interest as it springs from typical Bahamian sources.

Poetry

Much of Susan Wallace's poetry also springs from these sources. She is a well-published poet who is recognised by all Bahamians. Particularly familiar are those narrative and dramatic verses that capture the essence of Bahamian life. They often echo the ballad form and use authentic Bahamian speech patterns. Phrases such as, 'One woman get de Holy Ghos' (*Bulla Claudy Funeral*) present simultaneously the speech and elements of the life. The motifs are varied: *Islan' Life* emphasises the importance of community; *Ole Zeke* is an effective character poem. Such motifs and approaches are extended and paralleled by the other poets included in the anthology.

In *Decked in White and Black* Eddie Minnis describes the Bahamian policemen 'Adorned with red/And gold' standing 'In the shadow of/His blue umbrella'. The poem's imagery thus emphasises the contours of community. Telcine Turner-Rolle's poems are highly skilful in preserving traditional stanzaic patterns even as they use imagery drawn from local sources. She demonstrates a sophistication in the use of language resources in *Ode* in a number of ways, for example, in the repetition of the line, 'As scarlet leaves grow on Fort Charlotte grapetrees.' Her *Encounters with a Chickcharney*, is a delightful presentation in poetry of the image of a mythical Bahamian creature said to inhabit the central swamps of Andros, a creature that is a strange mixture of human, animal and preternatural. One stanza of the poem describes him thus:

> He had a queer and mixed-up form
> Like none I'd ever seen,
> His arms were bird, his ears were mouse,
> His legs were in-between.

Phylmos Hall's *Lament for a Li'l Old Lady* is a character poem, effective in depicting its subject. Another effective use of dialect narrative is found in Van and Gerry Oldham's *Punky's Place*. However, in the Oldhams' *Tools*, while the structure is traditionally poetic, the language is discursive, 'Our people are the tools of State,' as the poetic reverie is inadequate when one turns towards motifs of revolution.

Social motifs
Motifs of social awakening are abundant as in Dennis Knowles' *Political Farce*. And Mel Rahming uses the poem to move towards the language he advocates in *Black Resurgence*: 'He is here now, but he will speak tomorrow –/A new language – direct, potent and compelling.' He is effective when placing conventional images in the language of contemporary discourse:

> I have become entangled in the web
> Of my lines of jerky parallel
> And convenient repetition.   (*Strands*)

Both the prosy satire of Don Major's poem, *Sex* and the pathos in J.L. Mayson's *Little Barefoot Boy* critique social attitudes and actions. Cheryl Albury's poems focus on the socially-oppressed, the rejected infant, the woman. She presents images of women left to cope alone despite the physical presence of the men: 'And yet,/our weakness and our pride/go hand in hand/with anger–/to their beds' (*Poem for Mothers*). The passage is effective in its ability to portray the irony in the situation.

L.R. Malcolm's poems are placed in the revolutionary context but warn of the dangers of a false revolution:

> One evil has replaced another,
> Power and money have caused
> My brothers not to trust each other.
>
> (*In the Distance of my Mind*)

Norris Carroll's *'Cause the Arawak is Angry* echoes the old ballads in presenting a tension between the repetitive lyrical phrases that create a quasi-pastoral context and the violent denouement of the last two stanzas:

> runs a man berserk in vengeance
> lighting fires everywhere:

'cause the Arawak is angry,
That his people are not free.
In the quiet of the evening
By the Caribbean Sea.

Imagery

All of the poets use certain forms of imagery to buttress their motifs. This is particularly true of the work of Meta Davis Cumberbatch who uses formal patterns and nature figures (*Of 'The Barren'*). Vivid imagery allows Ashley Saunders to create images of the hermit crabs. When Kevin Andre Turnquist focuses on the confusion and loneliness in modern life, he presents contemporary objects in everyday language, making his tone ironic. Thus he uses the 8-track tape and the telephone as he describes a human figure 'revolted at his writhing coils/as he lies bleeding on the floor'. (*Crystal Clear Confusion*)

Basil Smith uses 'snowless winter' and 'dry thatch cottages' to describe a man isolated: 'Hatred for the thickness of my lips/And the memories of drums.' Liam Nelson's vivid imagery with its emphasis on colour emerges, no doubt, from his life as an artist. He provides some surprises as he rejects conventional uses of images for phrases like '... the chill claw fingers of the silver birch/is ice-frozen' or 'Soft bubbles whisper, while floating red and golden/kisses shower'. (*Now is Then*)

National pride, universal emotions

But such imagery is always in the service of the primary feelings of the poem. Robert Johnson, for example, often celebrates being a Bahamian. In *Sun in my Skin*, he asserts 'Cutlery confuses me' but counterpoints this in the second stanza with 'But in my brash vibrating arm/The cowbell dances.' Johnson uses nature images to catalogue the function of writers:

Stark is the picture that we must outline,
Bare as the shell in the sand,
White as bleached coral, coconut hard,
Black as the back of my hand,
We must get down to the root of things
To the root of the bread-fruit tree ...

(*Back to the Root*)

But in *Savacou* a pessimism emerges in the reiterated phrases: 'There is/No way back to the tribal dances,/No way ... no way back to the ancient/Ritual ...'

Generally, many of the poems assert the existence of a Bahamian culture and a Bahamian sensibility; Jerome J. Cartwright says, 'my soul/will not inhabit their Farawayland'. But if the soul insists that it can find fulfilment

11

in its own land, there is a feeling that such images may be shared and find their place in the whole. Cumberbatch writes: 'This land, with symbols through which I find/Blessings to share with all mankind.'

In *Taste of Apocalypse*, I suggest a tension between the paradisal perfection of an island landscape and the speaker's desire for counterpoint or polarities. In photographic terms, one must discover the verticals that will give form to the horizontal.

Patrick Rahming focuses on the authentic images of Bahamian life placed in a context of a social revolution that is a daily occurrence. Thus past, present and future inform poems such as *Still and Maybe More: A Trilogy*:

> perhaps the last, fierce
> big-bubbied Nango woman
> has climbed the hill
> and descended
> and seeped under the door
> like the smell of boiling guava
> into the Houses of Parliament
> where boiled crab and dough
> is now served
>   under glass

But Rahming's poems portray a variety of perception and feeling. In *Mailboat to Hell*, there is a strong lyrical quality girded by a localised image — the mailboat which alludes to the mythical ferryboat which takes the Greek dead to Hades. And Rahming's social concern is dominant in poems such as *Breakfast Bruise* and *Stranded*.

By making societies truly present, the writers help such societies to contribute to the growth of the community of peoples, the community of ideas, the community of artistic forms by which we truly see the world around us. Poetry is the re-enactment of a subjective experience but the re-enactment itself changes the mode of the experience. No longer is it the poet's private possession; it now belongs to the community, to the culture from which it emerged. By extension then, it is a gift to the world community, leaving a fragment of its own environment for posterity.

There has been no evaluation of excellence in these remarks I have made. I believe that for the present such comments would be irrelevant. For this anthology allows us to experience something that can transcend taste: a community of writers who present images of feeling in literary structures by which the Bahamian community can proudly begin the task of extending its political existence to a more permanent presence within the history of human civilisation.

1 | Prose

Smokey Joe Says - 1

Man, me an' Unkle Gabe wuz walkin' long Eas' Street d' udder night mooin' slow an' communin wid nature wen we see two gentlemen junp out one car an' start runnin. Unkle Gabe say, 'I dunno if dey runnin' towards sump'n but dey certainly in a hurry.' I say. 'Das Dr Straton an' Missa Philip Bethell. Dey gone in d' broadcastin' station. Dey mussy gon make a speech or sump'n.' Unkle Gabe say, 'I ain't bin in d' broadcastin' station yet.' I say, 'Well lemmuh take yuh up dere.' He say, 'Wait, lemmuh tie dis hankicher roun' muh mout'.' I say, 'Whut y' doin' dat fer?' He say, 'Ain't you say upstairs?' I say, 'Yeah.' He say, 'An' ain't you say one o' dem men is Dr Straton d' dentist?' I say, 'Yeah.' He say, 'Well if I goin' upstairs wid him I ain't gon take no chances. I ain't gon let 'im dash me down an' take out all my teet.' I bus' out laffin'. Unkle Gabe say, 'Whut you laffin' at? D'las' time I wus in a upstairs buildin wid a teet-puller wuz up t' Cat I'lun. I gone t' d' disqualified practician an' tell 'im I got a teet-ache. He look in muh mout' an' say, "Y' got a bad toot dere. I better take it out." I say. "I comin' back." He say, "No, y' gotty have it done now cuz da's a very bad toot." I start fer d' door an' dat feller grab muh. He dash muh down t' de top o' de steps, but he pliers in muh mout' an' start pullin' –an' wen he get dat toot out we wuz bote on d' downstairs front porch.'

I say, 'You get wex hey?' He say, 'If y' tink I wuz wex den– you shudda seen much wen I find out it wuz d' wrong toot.'

Well, wen we get up t' de top o' de steps one feller say, 'Where yinna goin'?' I say, 'In d' broadcastin studio.' D' feller say, 'Is you connected wid d' Bahamas Fair?' I say, 'We certainly is. Unkle Kiah is growin' a yard full o' stuff. Unkle Mel is bringin' a boatload of argricultural products an' divers an sunday exhibits from d' Babbie dig-fer-victory farm t' Cat I'lun, Unkle Gabe is makin' a special kine o' walkin stick an' I is comin' along t' help Unkle Kiah, Unkle Gabe an' Unkle Mel row wid d' committee if dey don't get firs' prize.'

D' feller say, 'Awrite, I guess you cud go in.' Wen we get inside I whisper t' Unkle Gabe I say, 'Now since we tell d' man we is connected wid d' Fair we can't back down. If dey aks us t' tawk we gotty tawk.'

So wen Dr Straton see muh he aks muh t' tawk, I say, 'Awrite, come on Unkle Gabe, tell um sump'n.' Unkle Gabe say, 'No, man. I can't tawk over no radio. I suffers frum microbe fright.' I say, 'Come on man, tawk.' He say, 'No I ain't gon say a word.' So Unkle Gabe sit down in d' corner o' d' studio eatin' peanuts out o' a bag in Missa Brown coat pocket - an' he had a gud time all by hesef while I do d' tawkin'.

Well tawkin' 'bout dis Fair me an' Unkle Gabe an' Unkle Kiah went up t' de Fair Grounds d' udder day t' look roun'. Man, hundreds o' peepul wuz all 'bout up in d' roof o' dese buildin' puttin' on tatch an' ting. Wen we get inside d' gate Unkle Kiah say, 'Da's a putty buildin' wid dem yaller an' blue stripes.' Unkle Gabe say, 'Yeah dat look like a real Fair buildin'. Remine muh o' wen I wuz t' de Cactus County Fair in d' United States.' So we aks sumbuddy whut dat buildin' wuz an' dey say Miss Carstairs buil' dat t' put all d' tings frum Whale Cay in.

Well we walk roun' an' roun' an' direckly we miss Unkle Kiah. We aks errybuddy if dey see Unkle Kiah an' errybuddy say dey don't even know 'im. Putty soon we see Unkle Kiah walkin' out one big buildin' wid Missa Lawrance. We hail 'im. I say, 'Unkle Kiah where you bin?' He say, 'I wuz jus takin a walk to dis Handcrafts Hall an' all on a suddin I get lost, so I seddown an putty soon I see Missa Lawrance pacin an' I say, "Well he mussy know howt' get out o' here." So I follow 'im - an sho nuff he did know how t' get out.'

So I aks Missa Lawrance where d' agriculture goin' an' he show muh a whole side of a big buildin'. I say, 'Poor, Unkle Mel. His boatload o' stuff he bringin' in d' sloop *Sarcastic* gon get los' in here.' Missa Lawrance say, 'Don't worry, we'll take care o' your Unkle Mel.' I say, 'On behalf o' Unkle Mel, I tank you.'

Unkle Gabe say, 'Well, I guess you'll have plenty games an' tings t' play hey?' Missa Lawrance say, 'Oh yes plenty. And we're having a ferris wheel and flying horses and a fashion show and a dog show and a flower show and tea garden . . .' Dat time Unkle Kiah interrupt 'im. He say, 'Go way Missa Lawrance, y' can't fool me. We don't grow no tea roun' here.' Missa Lawrance say, 'You don't grow tea in a tea garden. You drink tea in a tea garden.' Unkle Kiah shake he head frum side t' side. He say, 'Dese city peepul does do some funny tings. Dey don't grow tea in a tea garden, dey drink it.' He tink li'l while, den he look up at Missa Lawrance. He say, 'By d' same token, does yinna city peepul eat flowers in a flower garden?'

Well, it seem like tousands an' tousands o' peepul goin' t' dis big fair an' dey'll all have a opportunity o' seein' Unkle Gabe's latest invention. Unkle Gabe's walkin' stick is gon be one o' d' sensations o' de fair. I can't explain all d' unique features of it in a scientific manner but I will give yuh a general idea of its versatility in' Unkle Gabe's own words. Unkle Gabe say, 'It is delicately moulded by ambidextrous hands which respond to every command

14

of a brain which attaches paramount importance t' defence o'de body against aggression. D' stick is primarily designed,' he say, 'fer lickin' eny adversary over d' head – and accordin t' de rules o' chivalry it may be subsequently presented t' such adversary t' assist him in leavin d' scene o' de accident.'

Smokey Joe Says - 2

Well, bulla I hear diplomatic relations is becomin strained between Harbour I-lun an' Spanish Wells. It seem dat Spanish Wells want t' institute a school hall Putsch an' set up a central gubment which will reduce Harbour I-lun t' a vassal state. Well Harbour I-lun say dey know how t' push too if it cum ter a Putsch, so dey is gon insist on d' right o' self determination an' will mobilize all deir resources t' defen' d' liberty o' d' individual under deir constitution. So dey call a meetin under d' big tree an errybuddy seddown an' whittle sticks – an' by d' time dey get a pile o' whittlins high as d' abutment dey decide t' organize a Sassiety fer d' prevention o' Fift' Columnists. Spanish Wells say dey never did want war in d' firs' place cuz dey is a peace lovin' peepul but dey say deir neighbours has adopted a policy o' encirclement an' deir only course is t' demand economic freedom at d' point o' d' grains. So dey call a meetin' on d' cricket pitch t' decide wedder dey shud set up deir invasion ports on d' nort' side or d' sout' side – an' dey come t' d' conclusion dat it don't make no difference cuz dere's only two hundred yards in between. Well at two o'clock dis mawnin' d' Prime Minister o' Current call a emergency session o' d' Cabinet on d' sea rocks followed by a meetin o' d' High Command, an' at four twenty-five dey issue a statement t' d' effect dat Current will maintain stric' neutrality. It is d' opinion of observers at d' Bogue, however, dat Current will be unable to keep out o' d' conflic' fer very long. In d' meantime Tarpum Bay say she will supply conch shells t' Spanish Wells while Rock Soun' say she will trade two over-age fishin' smacks t' Harbour I-lun fer bates in her fishin' grounds. Savannah Soun' an' Palmetto Pint is watchin' developments. Governor's Harbour is urgin arbitration an' Hatchet Bay is prepared t' conclude trade agreements wid bote sides fer delivery o' foodstuffs on a cash an' carry basis.

Unkle Gabe say d' bes' ting fer Nassau t' do is t' adop' d' teory o' ol' Joe Stalin – sweet up errybuddy an' keep um goin' so dey can't get tegedder an' gang up on us. Unkle Gabe say if dey ever effect a Anschluss d' nex' ting dey'll do is begin disseminatin' propaganda 'bout d' mistreatment o' Harbour I-lun an' Spanish Wells minorities in Nassau an' if dat ever happen, he say Nassau is los. Unkle Gabe say dat seein as how our administrative departments is staffed an our public utilities is manned almost exclusively by Harbour I-lunders an' Spanish Wellsians, Nassau will inevitably be d' subject of a bloodless conquest. 'Sign solemn pacts wid bote sides an' break um or renew um at your convenience,' is Unkle Gabe's advice t' d' Nassau Cabinet.

Speakin' 'bout d' Nassau Cabinet. I went t' d' House O' Resembly d' udder night an' I witness d' dryest row in history. Missa Young get up an' say he want a statement made by d' Leader o' d' Gubment t' be included in d' minutes o' d' House. D'Leader say Missa Young ain't go no right t' do dat cuz his statement wuz a speech an' not a communication. Missa Young say it wuz a speech an' not a communication. Missa Young say it wuz a communication cuz d' Leader read it frum a piece o' paper. D'Leader say he read it frum a piece o' paper awrite but he didn't put d' paper down on d' table. Missa Young say he neverdeless wanted it t' go in d' book. D'Leader say he didn' have no right t' aks fer it t' go in d' book cuz instead o' puttin' it on d' table he put it in he pocket. Missa Young say he still wanted it t' go in d' book. So after d' Leader wuz finish havin' he fun he say d' facts o' d' matter wuz dat he put it in he pocket, den he len' it ter a member who forget t' return it an' d' Chief Clerk get hold of it an' aks him if he cud write it in d' book an' he tell 'im yes – so it wuz done dere enyhow.

It's d' same ting wid Harbour I-lun. Dey don't have t' argue 'bout where d' capital shud be – cuz it done dere enyhow.

I aks Unkle Gabe whut he wud do if he wuz approached by bote sides wid reference t' acceptin' d' post o' Propoganda Minister. He say he wud give d' matter due deliberation, concentration an' meditation an' den do like Dr Goebbels – disseminate propaganda fer one side an' put his money in d' bank on d' udder side.

Eh bulla?

Smokey Joe Says - 3

Unkle Gabe say he don't tink Muzzleasy is a Italian. He say he tink he mussy a Nassau man cuz while Missa Churchill an' ol Hitler tryin t' win d' war wid guns Muzzleasy tryin t' win it wid mout'. He jus' like dem fellers in d' House o' Resembly – d' bes' he cud do is tawk.

Whenever enyting happen in Europe Muzzleasy is d' firs' one y' hear frum. He only gotty hear sumbuddy else done sump'n an' right away he climb up on d' firs' piazza he get ter an' tell d' peepul all 'bout how he had a difficult time doin' it but how he finally accomplish his objec' by virtue o' his unsurpassed determination an' courage.

Man d' udder day Hitler an' Muzzleasy decide t' take Greece. Well, soon as him an' Hitler wuz finish tawkin', Muzzy run out in d' road, jump up on one piazza an' tell d' peepul whut he gon do t' Greece. D' Greek peepul tell 'im come try it. He say, 'Wait, I comin now.' He run over t' Hitler. He say, 'Dolfa, dese Greek boys say dey ready t' fight us. I tink you better go out dere an' beat um.' Hitler say, 'Not me. You wuz d' one who challenge um. You go beat um.' Muzzleasy say, 'Who me?' Hitler say, 'Yeah, you.' Muzzleasy say, 'I sorry I ever brought this up.' Enyhow, he figger he haddy do sump'n, so he sen he army down t' take Greece. Man, wen dem Greeks rush out o' dem mountains an' start shootin fas', Muzzleasy army turn roun' an' set d' course fer Rome. Erry day, all Hitler cud hear wuz how dem fellers wuz pickin' up speed. So finally he say, 'Muzzy, you better go out dere an see if y' can't do sump'n wid y' boys.' Muzzy say, 'Who, me?' Hitler say, 'Yeah you.' So Muzzleasy gone, an' when he get in one valley in d' middle o' Albania he meet all his army runnin towards im. Wen d' general pass 'im he reckernize Muzzleasy so' he look back over his shoulder an' say, 'Boss man, whut you doin here?' Muzzleasy say, 'I come t' lead yuh t' Athens.' D' general say, 'Dis ain't no time fer jokin, bulla y' better help us find a short cut t' Rome.' Well man, dat time d' Greek army broke tru d' valley. Muzzleasy look at um an' beat his fis on he ches', den he look up at d' top o' d' mountain – an' whut y' tink he see up dere? He see hesef. He say, 'It's surprisin' whut a man kin do when he make up his mind t' do it. I certainly got up dere in a hurry.' Well, bulla, putty soon he pass d' general. He say t' d' general say, 'Did you say you wuz goin' t' Rome?' D' general say, 'Da's whut I said.' Muzzleasy say, 'Den let it not be said dat d' great Beneety faild to lead you.' Now in d' meantime Hitler figger he better do sump'n quick t' help dis poor feller so he sen' d' whole German army roun' t' d' back an' ketch dis handful o' Greeks in a trap. But Muzzleasy wuz runnin' so fas' he didnt know whut wuz happenin'. Hitler haddy holler at 'im. He say, 'Muzzy, Muzzy!' Ol' Muzzleasy say, 'I ain't got time t' tawk now. Come up t' d' house some mawnin' wen I ain't busy.' Hitler say, 'But I stop dese fellers frum chassin' yuh.' Muzzleasy stick he heel in d' groun' t' slow up speed. He turn roun'. He say, 'Y' got un?' Hitler say, 'Yeah.' Muzzleasy turn t' d' general. He say, 'Well, whut y' stannin' dere pantin' fer? Find me a piazza quick.' So ol' Muzzleasy climb up on d' piazza an' congratulate he army on deir bravery an' efficiency an' congratulate hesef on leadin' his great peepul to a great victory. Den on d' strength o' d' victory he gone home an' confer two decorations on hesef.

Yeah, bulla, it seem like Muzzleasy does depen on mout' t' get 'im by an take he mind off he predicament. He remine me o' Unkle Mel. Man, one night Unkle Mel an' Unkle Gabe wuz walkin pas' one graveyard. Soon as dey get breast o' d' graveyard Unkle Mel start laffin' an wisslin' an' tawkin loud. Unkle Gabe say, 'Man shut up y' mout befo' y' get arrested fer misturbin' d' peace.' Man, Unkle Mel jus start t' tawk loud, tellin Unkle Gabe 'bout if he see a sperrit how he wud grab 'im t' find out whut he feel like. Well, bulla, dat time one almond drop cut one tree an' hit Unkle Mel on he heel. Man, he eye fly open like cash register. He foot start mooin fas' but wuzzn' gettin' nowhere. He say, 'Wait, foot le's approach dis matter sensibly an' get some cooperation in dis time o'stress.' He stop. He plant one foot in front o' d' udder, sway back an fort' tree times den misappear in d' distance. Wen Unkle Gabe get home he meet Unkle Mel settin' down in d' fambly circle. Unkle Mel say, 'Well, y' reach, hey Gabe?' Unkle Gabe say, 'Yeah.' Unkle Mel say, 'By d' way, Gabe, wen did d' Gubment put up dat big iron fence?' Unkle Gabe say, 'What iron fence?' Unkle Mel say, 'On d' way home I pass a tall iron fence wid a bright light on top o' erry spoke.' Unkle Gabe say, 'Man dat wuzzn no fence – dat wuz d' lamposts 'long Shirley Street.'

Yeah Brudder Muzzleasy is jus like dat. All dat watermelon-head feller does is jump up an' down an' holler t' keep frum gettin' scaird. Dis week he write in his noospaper dat him an' Hitler now considers d' United States deir enemy an' say Missa Roosevelt better look out dey don't sink his boats. I wud jus' like t' see ol' Muzzleasy if he wuz on a Italian battleship an dey fire a shell at a American boat an' miss it, an' den d' American boat turn on um. Muzzy wud say, 'Cap'n gimmuh dat wheel.' Wen Muzzy get speed up on dat battleship d' cap'n wud look tru he telescope an' say, 'Boss man I didn't know we wuz near d' Bahamas.' An' Muzzleasy wud say, 'Whut y' mean?' An' d' cap'n wud say. 'We bin passin' tru a string o' i-luns fer four hours straight.' An' Muzzleasy wud look at d' cap'n an say, 'Dem ain't i-luns, man, dem's continents.'

Eh bulla?

Eugene Dupuch

Veronica

If you've seen a bronzed maiden riding her bicycle down the middle of Main Street, you've probably come across my friend, Veronica. Did you notice a single blond braid falling down her back, bare feet, a silver earring with a Moroccan charm dangling therefore? Did you feel compelled to turn around and stare into those dark, misty eyes? If so, you've probably had the good fortune to become acquainted with my friend.

When I first met Veronica, she was swimming in the ocean – in fact, right in the Nassau Harbour area. She had been snorkling along the coastline collecting shell treasures and becoming acquainted with the various fish there. I had been strolling down the docks when I caught a glimpse of her lithe, tanned body in a chocolate brown bikini knifing methodically through the current. Within a couple of minutes, a smooth round face surfaced and a wide pearly-toothed smile was spread across it. As she smiled I noticed she had those immensely appealing sun lines around the corners of her eyes, giving her a well-seasoned look, like that of a swarthy sea captain. I recalled having seen her face before (probably on her bike in town) and felt I would like to strike up an acquaintance with this sea nymph. I meandered in her direction, and before long I had struck up a conversation with her, and we were sharing thoughts.

From that day on, Veronica and I were firm friends. In fact, within a week she had moved in with me. The boat she had been living on was leaving the island and, being stuck for a place to stay, I offered her a room in my house for a while.

She arrived at my front door one morning, clad in white jeans, turned up at the bottoms, and a scanty pink top. Her damp hair looked squealingly clean, and huge, round sunglasses adorned her nose, whilst a silver mounted tiger tooth and a large whistle dangled from a chain around her neck. Under one arm was tucked a plexiglass skateboard, the other supported a cassette stereo machine, and a frisbee peeked out of her canvas travel bag. I later learned that, along with a photo album, her passport and a couple changes of clothes, those things were her only travelling possessions.

Veronica has travelled almost everywhere in the world. As if that alone wasn't a great enough feat for a twenty-six year old waif, she rarely has more than twenty dollars in her pocket upon arrival at a new destination. She feels confident that people will help her out, should she need them! Generally, people will want to help her. They are drawn to her warm smile and fresh, wholesome appearance.

She can amuse you for hours with her tales of adventure all over the world. With stories of her sleeping under the date palm trees and the stars in the Spanish Sahara with her dog, Sid, and her capers with movie stars in

Mazatlan, Mexico, she'll keep your ears buzzing with curiosity.

Her photo album consists of intriguing photos of people and places, that lead you through the intertwined paths of her life. Filthy drunks asleep on a park bench in Paris, wild camels in the desert with sand mountains towering behind them, a surfer boyfriend on a seedy balcony in the North of Spain, where marijuana plants grew dense and tall around him, and a turbaned Indian throwing her frisbee, with Buckingham Palace looming up behind him, are all subjects in this photographic journey. Tucked in the back cover of the album is a receipt from a Mexican prison, given to her when she had to bail a friend out of jail for rowdy behaviour! This girl Veronica has seen it all!

Although Veronica rarely has a dollar in her pocket, should she find herself in a serious financial predicament, there's always her great-grandmother, who upon receiving a phone call from her drifter great-granddaughter will send fifty dollars to the appropriate corner of the Earth. Veronica never feels destitute. A sparkling diamond earring remains in her right ear as a last resort to obtain some financial comfort.

She was born and raised in Cape Cod, Massachusetts, where she worked as everything from a bar waitress to the first mate on Ted Kennedy's yacht. Veronica and her mysterious manner are well known on the Cape as she rides bareback on her cream coloured horse, Buttermilk, to and from her various jobs. Although she spends very little time in Massachusetts, she returns there every year at Christmas to partake in her parents' gigantic yule-tide celebration.

Veronica is attractive to a huge number of people. Every size, shape, creed and colour are drawn to her magnetic presence. She never turns away from the greeting of a stranger, no matter how seedy-looking he or she may be. As one can imagine, her naivety in this area has led her into some rather awkward situations. She is constantly being robbed, like no other person I have ever met, and her gentle trusting nature permits undesirables world-wide to take advantage of her in every way imaginable. However, should a situation become too uncomfortable for her, she is capable of fighting like a powerful, heavyweight boxer. Her tanned body shimmers with the muscles of a number of years' hard physical work.

A year ago, I somehow found myself in Paris with Veronica. Through her innumerable contacts we had crossed the North Atlantic Ocean on a private yacht to the South of France, eventually ending up in Paris. Throughout the trip Veronica never ceased to amaze me. I remember the time we were moored in Bermuda for repairs, Veronica had disappeared one morning, armed with her frisbee, and had returned with eighteen passionate French sailors off the Cousteau research vessel *Calypso*. She had charmed them all right off their feet, and they had followed her back to our boat, hoping for a beer.

In Paris we spent many hours in the various art museums and as she would attract the weirdos I would spend my time staring icily at them, hoping they would leave. One day, however, she went to a museum alone and returned later in the day to our hotel with a Greek. This particular stranger had invited us to dinner and, not wanting to be a wet blanket, I accepted reluctantly. After dinner, he drove us around Paris, and it was all very interesting. However, just as I was thinking that we had survived the evening intact, the fun began. The Greek walked us to our room and without so much as a hesitation, followed us inside. Veronica looked vaguely surprised as he began his advances towards her, and when he started to chase us lustily around the room, I lost my temper. I yelled down the hall desperately and help arrived. What an evening! The Greek left the room giving us a resentful backward glance.

Needless to say, nowadays I am a trifle hesitant about travelling with Veronica, although she has hitch-hiked from the North to the South Pole without a serious problem! One thing I can say, there's never a dull moment!

And where is she now? Who knows? I know that one day soon I'll receive a tattered postcard from some corner of the Earth and I'll recognise the delicate scrawl immediately, and the little drawings which accompany it, and I'll think of my unusual little blonde girl-friend with the misty dark eyes.

Melissa Maura

21

Market Street in the Thirties

In my neighbourhood I cannot remember any of the children ever being bored. I don't think we knew the meaning of the word. Maybe it was because we never expected to be entertained. Our natural interest and curiosity was continually fed within the boundaries of Market Street.

What must be one of the first dry cleaning shops opened in Market Street. It was owned by Mr Grant, a tall, handsome, hard-working man who smiled at the interruption of children.

The shop was small and seemed dominated by a large and intriguing piece of machinery. Two large padded ironing boards, one on top of the other, sat on a heavy iron stand. The top board lifted. We watched with fascination as Mr Grant would smooth a pant leg on the lower board, then lower the top one and press down. A loud hiss, and a snake of steam. Had the monster eaten the leg? No. The lid opened to reveal a perfectly pressed pant leg.

In Trinity Place, the late James Mosko had his wood workshop, and he also smiled at the interruption of children. Can you imagine our wonder as we watched him take a piece of mahogany and with art, skill and patience, cut, sand, carve and mould until it was transposed into a graceful, softly curving leg of a table or chair.

My most favourite place of all was my father's sponge rooms, where the Esfakis Building stands today, right next door to Veranda House.

It was quite a large piece of property. Three warehouses ran along the south and western boundaries, and the open yard was shaded by a magnificent avocado pear tree that every year was laden with delicious fruit.

In the largest of the warehouses, some twenty women wearing straw hats, and sucking on clay pipes, sat on boxes, clipped sponge and sang. My most poignant memories are of these voices raised in untrained but sublime harmony. Sometimes the songs were happy, sometimes so sad and troubled that I wept in sympathy, but without understanding. Often the workers sang in praise of God.

It is strange that though I have a fairly good ear for music I cannot remember one single individual song. I can only conjure up the voices, relive the scene, and again be deeply moved.

Two voices I remember particularly. That of Miss Dorothy, a tall, lean, stately woman with a rich, deep contralto voice very reminiscent of Marion Anderson. And also the voice of the foreman, Mr Adderley, tall, thin but powerfully built, with a sculptured face of great character. He sang a low basso. Years later, the songs of Paul Robeson sharply brought back to mind this wonderful man of my childhood.

Clipped sponge would be thrown into big round straw baskets about six feet in diameter. I would look for a filled one, climb in and nestle comfortably in the softness of the sponge, with that exciting smell of sea still pungent, and surrender my senses entirely to the beauty of the singing.

In a separate and smaller warehouse, a few feet away, my father and another group of his workers, all men, sorted the sponge in size and kind – the final step before baling.

At the time, there was a large sponging fleet in the Bahamas. Graceful sloops that reaped a rich harvest of fine sponge from our waters. The living sea life was hooked, allowed to die, cleaned, and brought to market at the shed at the foot of Frederick Street.

Sponge merchants, mostly Greek in origin, bid for lots by secret tender. I think my father was a leader in his field. He loved sponge and handled them with such care and respect that his marking 'GE' on a bale of sponge came to mean quality in many parts of the world. He shipped to the United States, England, France and Germany.

The final stage in the processing of the sponges after they were clipped, sorted and properly dried, was the pressing into bales. This was done in the smallest of the warehouses on the western boundary, and always with Mr Adderley in charge.

I was a little afraid of the giant press. It was a monster of a thing in iron – must have weighed tons. The base was an iron coffin four feet long, two feet wide, and two deep. One of the longer sides could be opened when clamps were released.

The coffin was lined with a burlap, with generous overhangs, and then filled with sponge. From above, two men turned the handle that lowered, along a thick spiral pipe, a solid plate of iron, four feet by two feet, and about six inches thick. This was lowered into the coffin, pressing the sponge into pancakes. More sponge would be added and the process repeated until the coffin was filled with pancaked sponge. Then the overlapping burlap would be folded over the top and sewn. The side of the coffin unclamped to release a perfect bale, to be weighed, banded in three places with rope for further security, and marked.

Sometimes Mr Adderley would allow me to mark the bales for him, a privilege which made me dizzy with pride, and gave me a sense of great importance.

In 1939 a blight destroyed our sponge beds. My father lost his beloved sponge and I, my warm and kind-hearted friends. The warehouses were empty and derelict; but walking through them alone, I could still hear the voices and the songs, sounds and memories that will be alive in me always.

There is no denying that time cannot stand still, or growth and progress be halted. But I often wonder about the sacrifices in human values which are necessary for the movement of a town into a city. Is the glamour and excitement compensation enough for the horror? I don't think so.

Ileana McDermott

Mr and Mrs Robinson

Mr and Mrs Robinson lived in a wooden house, fairly large, with a little shop in front; a kitchen separate from the house in back – in fact you had to walk down about half a dozen steps to ground level to walk into the kitchen. I suppose houses were built high above the ground on most seaside properties in case of hurricanes or flood tides.

At the back edge of the lawn, where the sandy beach started, there was a tall wooden tower – out of bounds for us children. As it had been built so long ago, our parents feared for its safety. That doesn't mean we didn't go up whenever we could sneak away.

The tower looked as if it had been made of a child's erector set. The ground floor was a proper room with one door with the sign 'Office' on it. To get to the top, there were ladders and perhaps four or five floors before one reached the top where the view was simply breathtaking – you could see the back of Hog Island from the tower – also at the top there were benches all around where you could just sit, relax and be cool.

The whole structure was built on stilts, and the 'office', when you got inside, was really the outdoor toilet, and the part where one sat had no bottom, which means that everything fell on to the beach and was washed to sea at high tide. Needless to say, we didn't swim on that beach – although it was one of the prettiest, softest beaches in our neighbourhood.

Mr and Mrs Robinson were both neighbourhood characters each in their own right.

Mrs Robinson was grey (they were both very old). She wore either grey or black dresses, had grey hair, grey eyes, a lined face and a slightly hunched figure. The kitchen where she spent most of her time was black – I could never figure out why it was so black. Years later, when I was grown up, my older brothers told me it was black because she cooked with wood and the kitchen, also made of wood, had never been painted, and the smoke blackened the wood. The walls were black, the floor was black, the ceiling black, tabletops, everything. And in this black kitchen, she cooked the most delicious food.

Every Saturday night, the rich people would come in their fancy cars and pick up pots of souse, boiled fish and other goodies to take home for Saturday night supper. My parents would often send us to get a pot of something nice as a special treat.

Mr Robinson was almost completely bald, a thinnish man and he was bent over to an extraordinary degree which got worse and worse the longer he lived. Near the end, he was almost bent from the waist and had to raise his head to peer up at you. He was the neighbourhood philosopher. He was always having arguments with my father – when they really had a hot point to discuss, they would climb to the top of the tower and not allow any children, or anyone else for that matter, to join them. We thought this was most unfair as if the tower wasn't safe for us, how could it possibly be safe for two grown men? One of the problems children have.

Mr Robinson used to annoy Auntie Bay every time he saw her. He would say, 'Hello there, Rocker. Still rocking along?' She would suck her teeth at him and mutter, 'He's got a nerve!'

Eunice Humblestone

Psychologically Speaking

As these thoughts came to me I started to think of changing times. That is, things are not the way they used to be. Some members of the family are living in the past and some are living in the present, not to mention those who are already in the future. If psychologically the family is all scattered through time like that, with a lot of different ideas bout different things there gat to be a lot of confusion in the family – life and all. So yer start to see why we must think seriously bout dis family life business.

My mind went back to bout fifteen to twenty-five years ago. It seems to me that most parents would be dat much older dan their children and dis is what I find. All we had was family life – most people a'in had nutting else so to speak. You had ma for sure and maybe pa too, but more times he was surer than you. Ya had auntie, and uncle, gramma, and grampa too, cousins, bulla and titer too, and most a' the time they were all in the same house with you. You were glad to have dem sometime because if dey were older dan you and had one job you might get lil sumptin too. And when they were not dere you used to miss dem and worry bout them. So you would get on your feet or your bike, or horse or buggy or dog and ting, and go look fer dem and share yer panny-cake or johnny-cake, sweet milk, grits, or peas, guava or rice or corn, fish or piece a meat or anything ya had. You a'in had nuttin and ya was sharing like crazy.

Ya used to have Sunday-go-to-meeting clothes and tennis shoes, handed down in the family till the last life left them. Ya school shoes were those God give ya and ya born with. Sometimes ya shared them 'cause ya carried a younger or sick or tired one upon ya back.

When ya lil house used to leak ya even used to share the old rags to plug up de holes. Ya even used to share the newspaper or brown paper bag to clean yaself when ya went to the outhouse, if ya had one.

Then if one a ya family was sick ya would make sure ya went to see um and carry some strong bark to bathe um in, ta bring de fever down; or give um some Irish moss to strengthen de back; or made sure he drink some pi-pi, with salt in it to help he cole and I woon mention what else ya might a give um to get um well.

I almost forgot to mention how the children used to play moon-shine baby together with pieces of broken plate and glass bottle. Then I remember how families used to sit around in the dark or with one lamp light and talk old story bout Brer Bookie and Brer Rabbie, and the family history and 'ting like dat.

So many tings come to ma mind now I can't keep up with dem. I just remember how de people used to leave dere house open and go bout der business and most a de time de'ain lose nuttin cause de'ain had nuttin ta lose, and beside that all a dem was one. Then if they catch the teef the family would crucify him anyway and they would cast um into outer darkness. How far could the poor fellow travel when he only had he two feet?

Dem days you used to get togedder for erryting, specially to live. I bet ya some a dem young set tink I talkin bout one foreign country. Sorry ta disappoint ya, is Nassau I talkin bout. On top a dis I believe all a yinner think the psychologist gone outta her mind – well 'tai'n true, and I still talkin psychologically bout family life.

Nowadays we forget since we gat so much tings in de family and don't tink bout other people no more – we even have to organise charity since we get so neglectful. Since we get so much house, and car, and food, and clothes and God knows what, and more than what a lot a ya all need. The family broke up, ya don't respect the wise ole head, nor any other kind a head. In fact yinner does put de ole people in institution and forget bout dem like dey do in dem same foreign countries yer does talk about. You talkin dem same kind a crazy talk bout young and ole don't belong together. I get one puzzle for you – if we'en belong together, they why God put us all here like dis.

Yer drive your car an ting ter work erry day and come home and stuff yer gut an ya don't find out whether yer other family gat enough to eat. Some a ya gat two and three car ter one house and ya won't go look for yer family. Some a dem people say de don't see yinner nearly as much as when ya ain had no car. Stay right there with ye selfish materialistic self – ya forget God doon like ugly; and a hope ter goodness you ain forget God too!

Well I know how yinner gat bad mind – yer mustee wondering what happen ter me. 'Tain nuttin more than what one Guyanese writer name Jan Carew done talk bout. I done bust out in mer native tongue. For a long time I keep twistin and turning and couldn write a word down. Then all of a sudden, bam! – I bust right out. Carew say ya must express yourself in words how ya think first. Fer heavens sake don't be fraid ter espress tings in yer own language, ya could always translate it into the formal English later on. But ter tell ya de truth I don't feel like translating it today. Ye think ya could forgive me this once? Brethers and sisters lemme use mer own language this once, it does feel good ya know!

Mizpah Tertullien

Cocoa Plumming

Brer Bookie and Brer Rabbie were playing under Rabbie's house when Bookie started to laugh and laugh. Brer Rabbie said to Brer Bookie, 'Man wha happen ter ya? Ya soun' like ya goin on the Crazy Hill soon.'

Brer Bookie replied, 'Man one big t'ought just fly up in ma head! Rabbie, le's go down in de bottom a Chippin'ham ta de cocoa plum bush.'

Brer Rabbie said to his friend, 'Man, I can' go les I ask ma ole lady, an she ain home.'

To this Brer Bookie responded, 'Man, what wrong with you? You always does worry 'bout erryting, an' ya does be so scared all de time. Das why I doon like ter fool wid you! Wha kind a man you is, boy? Why you so dumb? Time yer ole lady reach back frum werk we could reach back ten times a'ready.'

So Brer Rabbie agreed to go cocoa plumming. In no time they were in the bush. They found all kinds of cocoa plums – black ones, purple, white, all kinds, ripe sweet ones, half turned ones, and those which tie up the inside of your mouth. They packed their pockets full, filled up the inside front of their shirts, and even filled two brown paper bags which they had found mashed up on the ground.

Brer Bookie and Brer Rabbie were feeling on top of this world when their feet slipped and they landed right in the middle of the muddy earth, right in the swamp. You know that cocoa plum grows best in swamps. Yes, that beautiful fruit grows best in swamp land.

Well child, the two started to sink and Brer Bookie, playing big, kept his mouth shut while he prayed. He was afraid that he was in quicksand and would be swallowed up by the earth and suffocate to death.

Brer Rabbie started hollering for his mother, saying that he knew she had told him not to keep company with Brer Bookie and not to leave the house without her permission. He continued screaming, 'I know I do wrong, but God please spare ma dis time! I ain' goin disobey ma mudder no more.' Brer Rabbie really carried on badly with his pleas. 'Do Mamma! Do Mamma! Please Mamma, tell God ter have mercy on ye only son!!'

All during this time Brer Bookie did not open his mouth, playing brave. The two of them were dead scared so 'der perspiration was running down dere sweat' as they would say. In other words water was pouring off them, and they got so cold that they fainted away.

When they came to, they found themselves on the side of the road with a whole crowd of people gathered around them. They had no idea of where they were. Besides this, they did not have any cocoa plums. Would you believe that by the time the people looked at them again, Brer Bookie had disappeared. Nobody could figure how he got through the crowd without anyone noticing him.

Somebody recognised Brer Rabbie in the crowd and got help to take him home. They placed him on two sticks and carried him hoisted on their shoulders. When they reached around the government nursery corner and Brer Rabbie's mother caught sight of her son looking as if he was dead she put her two hands on her head and screamed, 'Lord, dis is my cross terday! I know suptin was goin happen. I had such a bad dream las night! Oh Lord God mer only boy child gone! Yer mean yer take mer only boy chile in trut'. No, oh no, dis can' be true!'

The fellows rested the stretcher down with Brer Rabbie on it and he stood up. When his mother saw Brer Rabbie's dirty clothes she caught her senses right away. She realised that she did not give Brer Rabbie permission to go anywhere. Then she made a quick switch in mood and broke off a branch from a tamarind tree nearby.

Brer Rabbie's mother put one beating on him saying, 'Aint I tell yer doon leave dis yard les I tell yer to?' Brer Rabbie kept jumping up all around answering, 'Yes Maam, yes Maam, yes Maam . . . ,' to the rhythm of the lashes with the tamarind switch. 'Den why you ain do as I tell yer?' 'Brer Bookie, Maam, Brer Bookie Maam . . .'

Then the mother took in with the shortness-of-breath and she stopped beating Brer Rabbie.

Brer Rabbie fell down on the ground with one thought in his head, 'I really dumb in trut ter listen ter Brer Bookie! Ma belly hurtin'ma, my skin on fire, ma clot'es tear up, an' I ain gat no cocoa plum! Ges wait till I ketch Brer Bookie!!!'

> That's why:
> It's best to listen to your parents,
> It does not pay to follow company.
> Not everything that sounds good is good.
> Watch the sweet talkers.

Mizpah Tertullien

An Eye for an Eye

The lights of Nassau disappeared astern, tiny yellow candles snuffed out as they fell behind the unseen horizon. Now only the signal light at the top of Fort Fincastle water-tower could be seen flashing once every five seconds.

There was no breeze. The sea was as calm as a sheet of glass. As the *Barbara Too* slid through the water the wash of the bow wave showed creamy white against the dark velvet surface. Peter, standing at the wheel, breathed the clean ocean air appreciatively. It was good to be at sea again. He peered at the compass and then, from long habit, glanced at the night sky. There was the Big Dipper just the right distance off the port bow.

Miles away to the northeast, a subterranean mountain top rose abruptly from 6000 feet. Most of its ten mile length was covered with coral reef that lurked treacherously just below the surface, an area avoided by mariners. At one place only, the mountain top jutted just above the surface. Here a small island had formed; a flat sandy island about a quarter of a mile long and three hundred feet wide. A few shrubs grew reluctantly, like hair on a bald head. A shallow pond barely twenty feet wide, in the centre of the island, was bordered by stunted poisonwood trees. Nothing could live here but birds and mosquitos. This was Devil's Cay.

'So far, all is well,' Peter thought, looking up from the chart. 'We should reach Devil's Cay about two hours after sunrise.' Putting on a nylon windbreaker against the night chill, he mused, 'I wish I knew a bit more about Mr Taylor. He really gives me the creeps. Why should he want to leave Nassau in darkness? And throwing hundred dollar bills around? But if he wants to pay ten one hundred dollar bills for two days' fishing I'd be a fool not to accept.'

The charter had been timely. A series of expensive engine repairs and fierce competition around the Nassau docks had almost put Peter out of business. Not that he would have cared a great deal. His daughter's death had killed the drive which made him the most respected member of the Charter Boat Association.

Peter glanced astern. The tower light could no longer be seen against the great dark stretch of ocean and sky. The *Barbara Too* was alone, a tiny moving island on the immensity of the Atlantic. A school of flying fish sailed across the bow, their wings showing briefly in the running lights.

Peter shivered slightly as he remembered his daughter Barbara and her happiness when the *Barbara Too* was given her name. Now she would never again be his first mate.

'Why did she do it?' Peter asked himself once again. There was no clear answer. A friendly island girl exposed to the pressures of her peer group in the confusing environment of a big city. Casual experimentation with marijuana had led to more daring use of heroin. 'After her mother died we became inseparable. Barbara was known as my shadow,' Peter remembered, nudging the bow back on course.

The telegram had been all the more terrible because it was unexpected. The flight to New York was an interminable nightmare and he arrived too late. An overdose of heroin resulted in an agonising death. The funeral in the cemetery beside the sea was a continuation of the nightmare and afterwards his reaction of rage and grief had almost consumed him. But time had helped. The aching loss was there still but his rage was now replaced by an implacable hatred of drug traffickers.

In his reverie, the *Barbara Too* had come off course and was making a circle over the dark surface. Confused, Peter attempted to get his bearings, but at that moment Taylor came on to the bridge. 'What the hell are you doing?' Taylor shouted.

Peter spun the wheel and brought the *Barbara Too* back on course as Taylor continued, 'You just be careful, you stupid bastard. You think I pay good money to have you stooge around in circles.'

'I'm sorry,' Peter said.

'Are you sure you know how to find Devil's Cay?'

'Yes, I'll have you there in the morning, as promised.'

'I'm going below now but I'll be keeping an eye on the compass in my cabin. You keep this boat on course, if you know what is good for you,' said Taylor, as he stamped off the bridge.

The hours went by slowly. Peter found it difficult to remain awake. When he was certain they were out of the shipping lane, he put the *Barbara Too* on automatic pilot. In the galley he made a thermos of strong and fragrant coffee and returned to the bridge. There was now a slight breeze and from far ahead the momentary flash of lightning.

When the coffee was finished Peter was wide awake. The eastern horizon lightened and then glowed and the sun slid out of the ocean, eased by unseen pulleys into the sky. Peter discarded his windbreaker and braced himself against a slight roll as the *Barbara Too* ran through foam flecked waves. Off to port a black rain cloud straddled the horizon.

About an hour after sunrise, the horizon ahead became slightly wrinkled. Soon Devil's Cay could be seen, like a thin pancake on the surface of the ocean. A mile off shore Peter slowed the engines. The dark blue of the ocean changed to a greenish blue just seaward of the cay. Nearer, brown patches of reef showed just below the surface. Peter brought the *Barbara Too* along the edge of the outer reef and into a narrow channel that wound in a U-turn to end in a cove with a depth of ten feet. The reef broke the ocean swell. Peter threw the anchor onto the grassy bottom and stopped the engines.

It was suddenly very quiet. Devil's Cay was still and brooding, a sea monster waiting for its prey. The sea birds appeared to have left. Peter dozed on a fishing chair. He was soon awakened by Taylor.

'O.K., I need your help,' Taylor said, in his loud, coarse voice. He was dressed in jeans, dirty T-shirt and cowboy boots. A gun was in a shoulder holster. Small, hostile, brown eyes stared out of an unshaven dirty face.

Together, they launched the small dinghy. Taylor climbed in and paddled toward the shore. He shouted back to Peter, 'O.K. buddy, you can forget the fishing. I'll be back soon.'

Peter went below and sat on the bunk. 'What is going on?' he thought. 'This guy is bad business.'

Peter found his binoculars, a powerful pair given to him by a grateful customer on landing a record marlin. Standing back from the porthole, Peter adjusted the binoculars and soon found Taylor. He seemed ten feet away and Peter, momentarily shocked, brought the glasses down.

Taylor was now ashore and seemed to be digging in the sand, just above the high water mark. Pausing, he looked back toward the *Barbara Too*. Peter could see his menacing glare clearly but was now certain that Taylor could not see him.

Taylor stopped digging. From the hole he lifted a number of small plastic bags filled with a white substance which he placed in a larger black garbage bag. Peter dropped his binoculars. 'Heroin! Heroin!' he gasped. 'What a bloody fool I've been. Taylor is a drug smuggler.'

Peter sat on a bunk, slumped over, his head held in his hands. His mind was in turmoil. There was still time to start the motor and leave Taylor on the island. But he must handle this himself, for Barbara's sake. He heard the dinghy approaching. He sat up straight. His usually mild face was set in solemn resolve.

'O.K., wakey, wakey, come give me a hand,' shouted Taylor.

Peter came on deck and held the dinghy alongside. Taylor was exultant. He clambered aboard clutching the garbage bag. 'One million bucks, buddyboy, one little old million,' he gloated. Placing the bag on the deck, Taylor drew his gun and pointed it straight at Peter's heart. His two small eyes regarded Peter with a baleful stare.

'Now boy, get the anchor up, we're leaving right now. And head for Gorda Cay. My plane will be there tomorrow morning. And move, you bastard, move.'

Peter started the motor, left it at idle, and pulled up the anchor. 'A plan,' he thought wildly. 'I need a plan.' He took as long as possible securing the anchor and then made his way back to the controls.

'O.K. let's go,' said Taylor, waving the gun. Peter suddenly knew what he must do. Taylor was just below him in the cockpit. Peter manoeuvered the *Barbara Too* until the bow was pointing toward the channel. Suddenly he put the throttle full ahead. The *Barbara Too* leaped forward and Taylor was thrown toward the stern, the gun flying overboard. Peter jumped from the bridge and grabbed at Taylor. A hand clawed at Peter's throat, held tightly, cutting off his breath. As Peter tried desperately to pull the hand away Taylor kicked him viciously in the groin. The *Barbara Too*, now out of control, hurtled toward the reef.

Through a cloud of blackness, Peter's brain whispered insistently, 'Get him overboard,' Grasping Taylor around the waist, Peter lifted with desperate strength, stumbled, and they both crashed into the sea.

As the two bodies plunged downward, Taylor released Peter's throat. Peter gulped sea water and, doubled over with pain, tried desperately to reach the surface. After what seemed a long time, his head came above the water. The roaring in his ears stopped. Taylor floundered in the water, about twenty feet away. The *Barbara Too*, now three hundred feet distant, crashed at twenty-five knots onto a jagged reef.

Peter swam slowly toward the beach and was soon able to wade ashore. Further down the beach, Taylor lay where sand met water. Peter looked toward the reef. The *Barbara Too* had slid off the reef and was now sinking in forty feet of water. Strangely, Peter felt only elation. The heroin would never get into the hands of pushers.

Peter stumbled to the high water mark and sat down. 'What happens now?' he thought. Some friends at the Yacht Haven in Nassau knew of his destination and he reasoned that a search would take place if he did not return in three or four days. This was the only chance of rescue. Devil's Cay was far from shipping lanes and airline routes.

He stood up and took off his clothes and spread them on a bush to dry. The sun was scorching hot. There were no mosquitos now but later there would be millions, buzzing and biting, so that a man could be driven insane.

Peter was now thirsty but he knew that the water in the little pond was contaminated by the poisonwood trees, which grew along the border. One glassful was lethal and could result in a slow tormented death, with grotesque swelling of face and limbs.

Taylor now came toward Peter. He had discarded the cowboy boots and shoulder holster. The bluster was gone and he looked bedraggled and pathetic. 'Well, I guess we're in this together,' he said. Peter looked across the sea to the horizon. His eyes were cold and distant. 'No, we're not,' he said, 'You're on your own.'

Even though Taylor appeared subdued, Peter knew he could not be trusted. He would keep well away from him. Peter walked along the beach to the other side of the island.

It was mid-afternoon, with the sun scorching down from a hot blue sky, when Taylor discovered the small pond. He threw himself on his stomach and scooped water into his mouth. It had a sweet stinging taste and soon his eyes began to smart and redden. His eyes were soon forgotten as now the mosquitos rose in clouds and bit him savagely. As darkness approached, their numbers increased until Devil's Cay was under a ravenous swooping cloud. Taylor ran in circles moaning and slapping at the mosquitos until finally he took refuge in the sea. But even there the pitiless mosquitos covered his head and face.

On the other side of the island, Peter had gathered leaves from the wild geranium, of which there was an abundance. Crushing the leaves between his palms he smeared the pungent juice over his face, arms, legs and clothing. He massaged it into his hair. The effect was miraculous. The mosquitos stayed a foot away from Peter, halted by an invisible barrier.

Darkness was now complete. The stars were hidden in an overcast sky. From where he sat, just above the high water mark, Peter could barely see where sand met sea. His throat was parched and his thirst insistent. 'It is now time to find water,' he thought.

Kneeling, he scooped a wide hole in the sand. It was slow, hot work. Often it was necessary to pause and apply more wild geranium juice. But the hole became two feet deep and then three. Finally, at four feet the sand became moist. Hurriedly, throwing out the damp sand, Peter enlarged the area so that water could filter into a makeshift well. Soon he was able to scoop double handfuls of water into his mouth. It was cool and fresh and delicious. He remembered that his father had told him how the layers of sand act as a filter, removing the salt. When he was no longer thirsty, he covered the well with driftwood and twigs.

Peter now dug himself into the sand and applied wild geranium to his face and hair. His sleep was restless and dawn was welcome when it finally came. A cool sea bath revived him. He sat in the shallow water and watched the sun climb into the sky. The waves ran gently up and down the sand.

Suddenly his reverie was broken by a sound from beyond the reef, a sound that was unmistakably the throb of engines. Scrambling to his feet, Peter saw the long shape of a boat, which he recognised immediately as the police boat *Eleuthera*. White-uniformed figures were already launching a dinghy.

Finding their way through the reef the sailors brought the dinghy close to the shore. Police Superintendent Carey jumped on to the sand, followed by two armed policemen.

'Man, I'm glad to see you,' said Peter.

'Where is the *Barbara Too* and what happened to Taylor?' asked the superintendent, as he ran to the top of the beach and looked quickly around. Peter explained briefly the events of the previous day.

'It all fits in,' said the superintendent. 'We were tipped off that Taylor, using one of his many aliases, had chartered your boat. The boys at the Yacht Haven told us you were headed for Devil's Cay. So we put two and two together.

'Now where is Taylor? Carey continued. 'We want to get our hands on him.'

They found Taylor lying on the sand at the far end of Devil's Cay. But it was too late. His face and arms were swollen and hideous and he was quite dead.

As the dinghy went back to the *Eleuthera* Peter looked down at the blurred shape of the *Barbara Too* which had found her grave in the reef.

'There she'll stay,' he thought. 'She'll be an undersea monument to Barbara and, in a way, to Taylor as well; as good and evil seem to come in equal portions.'

As the *Eleuthera* sped away Peter looked back at Devil's Cay as it shimmered and brooded in the morning sun. Quickly the cay diminished and was soon lost in the immensity of sea and sky.

Chester Thompson

Ordeal at Sea

The wind, blowing out of the north-west lashed the tall cedar trees. They bent low, as if they would give way, but held fast. The row of trees along Front Street had been planted as a wind-break and they were now performing their duty well. Waves beat against the abutment and sped archlike out toward the sea after running along the curved surface of the sea wall. The wooden dock creaked as the heavy seas pounded the old planks. Rain fell in torrents, and the night was cold.

The residents of Carib Cay, all 572 of them, made their way toward Front Street. They held on to each other, lighting their way with kerosene lanterns. They came from all over, to stand in the rain, weather the storm, and to pray for the souls of those at sea.

Together they stood beneath the cedar trees with Father Clarke and prayed. They prayed for all at sea but especially for the men from their village who had not yet returned. The fishermen had all come in but Captain Elliott James, his son Myron, Dr Tucker and Mr Cooper had not returned from their afternoon sail in the sleek twenty-four foot sloop, *Miss Jane*. They had taken her on a trial run. The vessel, built by Captain James and his son, was entered in the Exuma Regatta, scheduled to be held only a fortnight away.

Charlie, the settlement drunk, with a rich baritone that carried through the gathering and out into the cold darkness of the stormy night, raised a tune. He had started the same hymn on such occasions for as long as he could remember. Everyone joined him. They sang with their whole being, their hearts filled with hope. They warmed each other, and despite the wind and rain, they were not cold.

> 'Eternal Father strong to save,
> Whose arm hath bound the restless wave,
> Who bids't the mighty ocean deep,
> Its own appointed limits keep,
> O hear us when we cry to thee,
> For those in peril on the sea.'

The group sang, prayed and did vigil throughout the night.

Aboard *Miss Jane*, the four men held on tightly. The waves tossed the boat about but she fought to stay afloat. Myron kept a firm grip on the tiller and with the skill of a master seaman, he guided *Miss Jane* among the restless waves.

'Daddy, we're too heavy,' he shouted above the roar of the seas.

'Yes, I know,' Captain James roared back, with a booming voice that seemed to have its beginnings in the deep recesses of his belly. Captain James was sixty-two, but sailing, boat building and hard work on his farm had kept him in good stead. His eyes stared into the darkness, but he saw no light from shore. He knew he had brought *Miss Jane* too far out to sea, and now, no matter what, the only hope for survival was to ride out the storm. It was foolish of him to take such a chance after listening to the weather report, but the fellows at the Meteorological Office were hardly ever right. Why did they have to be right this time? He held fast to the mast, his left arm wrapped tightly around it – his right he used for motioning his crew.

Dr Tucker and Mr Cooper were busy bailing water. As they threw one tinful overboard, the seas replenished the boat's supply. *Miss Jane* bounced, twisted, lunged forward and groaned, but she stayed afloat. Waves hit her bow and climbed toward the heavens, falling all around her and filling her bilge. The two men could not keep the water level down. It rose inch by inch.

Mr Cooper, a fat bachelor-politician, wished he were back in Nassau. He longed for Cassandra's Pub, his friends, the party circuit, his posh home, his office and his secretary. His secretary he longed for most of all. He wished he had never invested funds in the building of *Miss Jane*.

The first place Regatta trophy he had always wanted to win, now seemed unimportant. But racing boats was a pleasing hobby and, as hobbies go, did not cost him much anyway. He tried to think of nothing – but his back ached and his arms were tired and breathing was not as easy as it appeared for the others. His pace slowed but he kept bailing. It was not his nature to stop – he hated giving up but, most of all, he hated losing.

Dr Tucker felt sick. He wanted to vomit. The heaving of the boat reminded him of the ride between Mandeville and Montego Bay. He studied in Kingston at the University of the West Indies. He enjoyed his stay in Jamaica, except for the ride over the hills in the centre of the island. Now he preferred the flat terrain of his native Marsh Harbour, on the island of Abaco.

He thought of Monica and as he bailed, he smiled.

'What the hell are you grinning about?' Sam Cooper yelled to him.

'Shut up and bail,' the doctor told his brother-in-law. It was only six months ago that he and Joycelyn were married, in a beautiful ceremony in the little church at Lowe Sound, Andros, where Joycelyn was born.

His thoughts kept rushing back to Monica. Joycelyn, his wife, he loved dearly, but he was intrigued by Monica's tall elegance, her beauty and her exuberance in living life to its fullest. He had met her at school – they were both medical students – and their friendship grew. She was brilliant, he was not; he liked dominoes and pool (she always insisted he was playing billiards); he hated horses, she sat a horse as though she had somehow become a part of the horse's anatomy – they moved as one, Monica and Topaz, her palomino mare. Monica was beautiful, pleasing to the male eye and the envy of every woman. She was the daughter of a wealthy planter. He was a bungling student, the sixth son of a poor Abaconian farmer, on a Government Scholarship. Their relationship was destined to come to an end.

He remembered the day it did. They had just come in from a long ride. Monica dismounted and asked a servant to rub Topaz down. He slid from his mount and handed him over to John, the stableboy, and followed her toward the house.

'I'm going to New York for summer,' she told him.

'How long will you be? I was hoping you would come to the Bahamas this summer.'

'Maybe after New York. My brother has been appointed Ambassador to the United Nations and I've promised to help him set up house.'

'Yes I heard. Would you offer him my congratulations. I suppose I'll see you next term.'

'Yes, of course.' She turned. He stared into her eyes and as she tossed her flowing hair, her brown face glistened in the afternoon sun. Amber breeches snuggled tightly to her frame while a white silk blouse hung freely, with the top two buttons undone. The heels of her high leather boots clicked as she turned and walked toward the house.

The next day he left for Nassau. He never saw her again. She wrote, only to tell him she was engaged to marry the Honourable Isaac Macumba, the celebrated Foreign Minister of one of the newly independent African nations.

'Gentlemen,' Captain James said as he swayed from one side of the boat to the other, 'one person will have to be towed. With a little less weight we may be able to ride out the storm. I'll pick the first person and he will tie a rope around his waist which will be made fast aft. We shall each remain in the water for two hours. Remember gentlemen, when in the water, your only duty is to keep your head above the waves.'

Captain James studied the members of his crew. After a long pause, he pointed. 'You're it, Mr Cooper. May the good Lord protect you.'

Mr Cooper picked up a coil of rope and tied it around his waist. He took off his sandals and started toward the side of the boat.

'Give me that rope,' Dr Tucker said as he tugged at him. 'You're too fat to last ten minutes out there. All this time I've been giving you free medical advice, you haven't listened at all. Beginning now, you pay.'

Dr Tucker made ready and jumped overboard.

'O.K. Doc?' Myron yelled.

'Yeah, I'm O.K.'

The storm continued to rage and the little boat and her crew desperately tried to stay afloat. Captain James and Mr Cooper bailed and Myron manned the tiller. *Miss Jane* had been given a deep keel, which kept her balanced on the angry sea.

Myron and his father had built *Miss Jane* from scratch, as they had many boats. Their living room was decorated with sailing trophies, which the older Mrs James polished with daily regularity. They were a renowned boat building family; their praises sung throughout the Bahama Islands. His great grandfather had started the family boat building business. His father had been taught by the old Captain James, as he too had been instructed and was now teaching his son.

'Help! Help!' Dr Tucker yelled between coughs. The three men hauled desperately on the tow rope, while Myron balanced the tiller with the ball of his left foot. When they got him aboard, it was too late. The good doctor could not stay on top of the mountainous waves, despite his youthful strength. He had swallowed too much water. Captain James cut the body loose and Dr Tucker was swallowed up by the sea.

The three grief-stricken men, without giving thought to their plight, remained too long to starboard. As a fierce gust of wind and a tall wave seemingly attacked *Miss Jane*, her mast broke, damaging her starboard quarter. The sleek craft capsized. Her three remaining crew members were left to fight the mighty waves which constantly attempted to bury them in a grave of an endless expanse of water.

Miss Jane may have floated, hull upwards, had she not been damaged by the falling mast. She went down, never to be seen again. The raging seas had won their battle – a minor victory, but a victory all the same – the sleek sailing craft had been defeated.

The three men spotted the mast and together they made for it. Mr Cooper and Myron were the first to grab hold. Captain James, farthest away, arrived winded. They held on for dear life as the seas raged about them.

The first light of dawn peeped through the dark clouds and, in the distance, as they rode the waves, holding on to the mast, the men made out the shoreline.

Shortly after sunrise, the winds quieted down and the seas calmed. The settlement folk, heads lowered, dragged themselves home to wait. Out at sea, the three men felt relieved.

It was well past mid-day. The sun was at its fiercest. Seagulls hovered above the mast and its three passengers, now cold, numb and with heads that ached in the early afternoon heat, continued to hold fast to the mast. Boats could still be seen searching the seas for *Miss Jane* and her crew, but none were close enough to call. The boats had left shore with first light.

Myron gave a scream and was gone. He surfaced twenty yards away.

'Daddy!'

'Myron!'

'Get me, Daddy, I can't move. Cramp. My legs. My arms.'

'I'm coming, son,' Captain James said as he swam toward his son.

'Captain! Leave him alone. He'll drag you under if you touch him,' Mr Cooper shouted. Captain James stopped midstream. He pedalled, looking first at Mr Cooper then at his son.

'Daddy, help me!'

'Captain, stay where you are,' Mr Cooper yelled again.

'Please, Daddy! Daddy! Daddy!' Myron cried as he slithered beneath the water. Captain James went back to the safety of the mast. He did not speak to Mr Cooper.

Hours went by as the two men drifted. The sun dropped behind the horizon and the sky darkened. It was a relief to be rid of the blinding sun, but as the evening wore on it became cold. The men shivered, but still they held on to the mast, in utter silence.

They did not realise until they were groping around trying to stay afloat, that the mast was sinking – it had become waterlogged. They loosened their grip and paddled to stay on the surface of the now peaceful sea. The mast surfaced slowly but as they tried to hold it, it again went below the surface. The two men knew it could no longer hold them both. Maybe one of them would have a chance of survival. Without the mast to support their weight, they both would die at sea, as although lights from the Cay could be clearly seen in the distance, land was too far off.

As if signalled to action, the two men made for each other. They fought fiercely, beating with their fists and kicking. After what seemed an eternity, both men, exhausted, ceased fighting. With his last bit of strength Mr Cooper swam to the mast and hooked his arm around it. The mast floated. Captain James stayed on the surface as long as he could. When his strength gave out he merely let himself sink. He felt as though he were floating freely through space, and then, it was all over. His spirit flew and he went down into the depths of the sea.

Mr Cooper kept a firm grip on the mast, hoping for a miracle – his only chance of survival he felt. The night had gone by and the sun had come out to shine again. He was numb and very weak. He could feel the warmth of the sun penetrating his aching head and shoulders and the glare caressed his face. His eyes opened but he saw nothing.

His feet dragged against something solid and he tried to stand. He fell. He raised himself slowly and, with much effort, made his way to more shallow water. When he could no longer hear rushing water about his feet, he allowed himself to fall exhausted to the ground. In the distance, he heard the voices of children at play.

Colin Tatem

Dog

Dog was the street's beggar. No one seemed to remember how he'd gotten that name. He remembered his real name, though. Lester Harold Ferguson. No one knew how old he was. He had been around since I could remember, living by begging food, appropriating a little money whenever the occasion presented itself. He slept under an old deserted house about five yards down from where I lived. He always wore the same ragged pants, black and gray with age, a yellowish shirt in holes from wear and a hat, squashed beyond recognition. He never wore shoes. On occasions he wore a red bandana tied elegantly around his throat and pieces of a tyre tied on his feet.

His hair was thick and red, matted with years of dirt. He had a broad nose, thick lips and small eyes. His eyes were his most arresting feature, if you looked at them closely. They were the saddest, yellowest and wisest eyes I had ever seen. Sometimes they had a wistful look and sometimes a mean look came into them.

Sometimes when I passed him on my way to school, he would look at me fiercely and say, 'You getting the education, hey? Wonder where it goin' to get you!' Then he would laugh loudly and slap his hollow chest. People in the street tolerated him. Seldom was he chased away from a back door.

I think I must have been about thirteen years or so when I first became curious about Dog. I asked my mother why he was called Dog. She replied because he acted like one. She said when he first had 'troubles' everyone would try to help him by offering food, money, or somewhere to sleep.

He accepted at first then started to refuse. Offers still made were rejected bitterly and, finally, with loud swearing and snarling so that people finally left him alone. I started to question her again but she said since I wanted to know so badly, to go and ask him myself.

I wondered if he ever slept. I wondered if he ever thought, and if so, what did he think?

One afternoon as I was playing ball in the street with Eddie, Bouncer and Truman – against my mother's orders – the ball rolled to where Dog sat. He picked it up as I was reaching for it. I stared at him and he stared back at me.

'See this ball?' he asked. 'This is life. A circle. All goin' round and round and comin' back to the same spot.' I grabbed the ball and ran back to finish playing.

That night, lying in bed, I wondered if his mother was alive. If so why did she not come and help him? If my mother died, would I get to be like Dog? The thought frightened me. I got up and went to check, to make sure that my mother was alive. She was sitting down, mending a pants of mine.

'What you want?' she asked.

'Are you all right, Ma? I mean are you sick or anything?'

'What's the matter with you boy? Go back to your bed.'

For the next few weeks I wondered about Dog. I wanted to find out why he lived as he did. One Saturday morning I sneaked out of the yard while mother was not looking. I found Dog under his floor and crept under with him.

'Ah, is you,' he said. 'What you want?'

We stared at each other. I was suddenly tongue-tied.

'You want to know if I sleep? If I bathe? How I live?'

I started to back off.

He said, 'Stay. Listen to me.' A faraway look came into his eyes.

'A long time ago I was married, happily, to a lovely young woman. Life was good. We had been married for four years and had two children. I worked at that time for an accounting firm, as a junior accountant. One day at work the phone rang and someone said that it was for me. The voice on the other end of the telephone told me to come to the hospital quickly, as my wife had been involved in an accident. I rushed to the hospital, but I was too late; she was dead and only myself and the two children remained. Someone had hit her with a car and had not even stopped. I buried her, feeling numb, numb. I took to drinking. I lost my job. The bank took my house and car. The state took my children as I was not in a fit state to care for them and I would not let anyone help me. I scavenged for food in garbage cans. That's how I got the name 'Dog'. I steal and beg money for drinks of fire, which helped me to live in an unfeeling state. My son must be your age now. One of these days I will pull myself together and start a new life.' He sighed.

'Come with me for some food,' I said impulsively. He grumbled a bit but finally said yes.

When we got home, Ma said, 'Who this is you draggin' in here now?' She turned from the sink and said, 'Why, Lester, 'tis you. Decide to join the human race again, hey? You look like you could sure use a good meal right now. Hey! Joan! Harriet! Mumsy! Come see!'

All my mother's gossipy neighbours came. They all stared and stared and stared and then went quietly away. They came back carrying clothing and food. Mumsy cut Dog's hair and they made him take a bath. He started to cry – great sobs which frightened me, for I thought that those sobs would tear his chest, thin as it was, apart.

He slept at our house that night. I got up earlier than usual the next morning to greet him and talk to him, but he was gone.

I never saw him again.

Antoinette C. Smith

Where is it?

The island of New Providence boasts two main ridges of hills, running east and west of this somewhat oval island. The range to the north enjoys no particular name, and is situated only a half mile or so from the northern shore, and for a great deal of the length of the island, it is within a hundred yards or less from the coast.

The old city started in the area that contained the widest space from the sea to the crest. On the highest point of the ridge was built Government House, and though it rises less than a hundred feet above sea level, it is labelled with the imposing nomina: Mount Fitz William. The business centre of the town was, and still is, Bay Street, which ran along the northern shore, and contained the hubbub of the little town. Running east of Mount Fitz William was East Hill Street, and west of it obviously was West Hill Street, and so they are called to this day.

About two and a half miles south of the northern ridge, exists another range of hills. These are known as 'The Blue Hills'. It is possible that they acquired this name long before they were explored, for looking at them from the distance of Mount Fitz William they appear blue, in the dewy haze of a morning. These hills are sometimes referred to as Baillou Hills, and the name Blue Hill might well be a corruption of the name Baillou. Perhaps some daring adventurer, whose name was Baillou, chose to live up there and anybody who chose to live that far from the harbour in the days when Nassau was first settled had to be a daring adventurer.

Between these two ranges of hills is a flat fertile valley. Traversing this valley from north to south is Blue Hill Road and in the beginning, this was the only road that pretended to take people from the sea on the north, to the interior of this island. As the population of the island grew, the people were settled in this valley and Blue Hill Road extended itself bit by bit, until today it runs from sea to sea.

In the days of the early settlers, from 1650–1850, this valley was mostly bush, sparsely populated, and unexplored. Uncultivated, and completely flat, it served as an ideal area to house the slaves, the Blacks who serviced the city and the 'rich and the well-to-do' who lived on the top of the hill to the north. A Royal Governor, H.E. Lloyd Grant, laid out in 1821 along Blue Hill Road (and about two city blocks on either side of it) an area known as Grant's Town for the purpose of settling those Blacks who serviced the city. This extended down as far as Meadow's Street and over westward as far as West Street.

These were the early Black settlers and later on in this work it will be shown who they were and how they came to be.

Let us now endeavour to keep in the mind of the reader the area described above known as Grant's Town. Let me (again) reiterate that it was populated by the 'Black' early settlers. The history of the time and the economics of the time demanded that more and more Blacks had to come and had to be settled. Thus Bain Town came into existence. It will also be explained later how and where, these settlers came from, and why they were settled there.

Bain Town has physical boundaries; these might be arbitrary and different according to who is defining them. Technically, it may be said that it is that area of the valley which was originally settled by Yorubas. This area was bounded on the east by West Street, on the west by Nassau Street, with extensions running about two blocks south of Meadow's Street, to include Yorubas of consequence who might have resided there.

It is a well known characteristic of Yorubas, wherever they are found in numbers, to cluster themselves together. They are not given to well-defined plots of land, and they have a tribal abhorrence for fences. Bain Town conformed, in the main, to this pattern and except for those streets that run from north to south the area is criss-crossed by a network of alleys, lanes and 'corners' giving great evidence to the heritage of its inhabitants. These byways were not officially named as they are today. They were dubbed with the names of the most prominent of their citizens, or the activities that took place in their vicinity. Hence these names were changed by generation after generation. Some of the names stuck and became the official names that they bear today, and so we have signposts that display such colourful names as 'Rupert Dean Lane', 'Dumping Ground Corner', 'Finlayson Street', which is locally known as 3Ps Corner, and 'Eneas Lane'.

These 'Streets' were originally meant for pedestrian traffic, formed by the constant tramping of human and animal feet. To me these were beautiful streets. The main streets were made of white limestone and, though narrow by today's standards, were comparatively straight. There was no need for sidewalks, and where they normally would have been, low growing weeds, grass and wild flowers grew. The side streets, narrower still, constituting mainly alleys and lanes, were more picturesque. Most of them consisted of two well-trod parallel paths, with grass and low bushes in the middle. These paths were made by the wheels of our horse-drawn vehicles, carts, drays and carriages. Far down through these lanes and on these streets lived 'the people'.

Meadow's Street was the 'main drag', and the centre of Bain Town which lay between West Street and Nassau Street. It was often referred to by the people who lived down through the lanes, as 'the Big Road'. On either side of this street were the homes of the more prominent people of the area and I have always thought that their prominence was due to the fact that they got there first. The homes were comfortable, brightly and pleasantly painted or 'whitewashed'; not too generous in size, but for the purpose for which they were built of adequate size, usually about a hundred feet square more or less, but most of the dwellers of the time took pride in their 'yards'.

On the main streets of Bain Town, and especially on Meadow's Street, these 'yards' were separated from the road by attractive walls of some sort interspaced by decorative pillars that held them together as ties. Many of these walls were made of limestone rocks which were plentiful in the area. The inhabitants were skilled in building rock walls, some of which have been known to stand for almost a hundred years. Behind these walls, easily visible to passers-by, were gardens. Though their construction and arrangements smacked strongly of the rustic, they were nevertheless expressions of the love of beauty, colour and neatness inherent in these people. A well-defined walkway, separating clusters of native rose bushes (seven sisters, they were called), multicoloured crotons, lace plants, or match-me-if-you-can shrubs led from the gate to the verandah. From this walkway ran paths through the garden to the back yard.

If the back yards were large enough, and most of them were, there was a kitchen garden there. In it grew pigeon peas, corn, sugar-cane, okras and peppers; and there was usually a bread fruit, an avocado tree, and the ubiquitous coconut.

Irrespective of the size of 'back o' the yard', there were certain essentials present. There was a well, an oven made of rocks and mortar, a kitchen and an 'out house'. A stand made of wood stood next to the kitchen for the washing of dishes, and next to it was the ever present 'lye barrel'. A 'lye barrel' was an essential before the days of the sophisticated detergents that we have today. It was a barrel, water-tight, half-filled with water. Into this barrel were thrown the ashes from the wood stove that was generally used. These ashes gave the water a sharpness that caused it to lather easily with the 'octagon soap' that was commonly used for the washing of dishes. Water from the 'lye barrel' mixed with the water from the well and 'octagon soap' and 'greasy bush' leaves, made for the sanitation of dishes that these people required.

The more industrious of my people added to these essentials in accordance with their space: a chicken coop, a pig's pen, and a goat or two. Most of the 'yards' of Bain Town had these essentials and the size of the plot dictated the distances that separated them. However, none was so far away that the odours that emanated from each were not mingled to make what I always have chosen to call 'the odour of home'. This odour to this day is indefinable by me and only those of us who grew up in Bain Town can even conceive of what I mean when I speak of 'the odour of home'.

I have since tried to analyse this odour and, in reflection, I have come up with what might be a plausible analysis. Here, I would have to be given the leave to describe the producers of these various odours separately. Take the oven; it was a stone structure of varying height, topped by an arched dome with one opening. In large families, this dome was separated into two compartments by iron bars making a shelf. To seal the opening was a wooden door, faced with tin. To further seal this oven, this door was 'chinched' with crocus sacks which were dampened. Wood of any kind was placed in this oven and allowed to form coals. When the coals, sufficient in quantitity and heat, were ready, loaves of kneaded dough in special pans were placed in and baked. I have found that the majority of the wood that was used for this purpose was the wood of the pigeon plum bush, and this has an aroma that is pungent and sweet. In spite of the door and its seals odours permeated the air and that of baking bread is beautiful.

The preparation of food within the dwelling house is a new innovation to Bain Town people. The kitchen was always in the 'yard'. Sometimes it was a substantial building but there were many that were simply 'lean-tos'. In the less sophisticated kitchens a stone constructed hearth was built and a fire made on it over which the food was cooked in three-legged pots. By the time I came along, there were many kitchens that had stoves that burned wood as fuel. A chimney protruded from the kitchen to carry off the smoke. Again most of the wood used for this purpose was the pigeon plum wood.

There was no refrigeration; and in order to combat this inconvenience food was mostly cooked and consumed the same day it was killed or plucked. Another way of combatting it was to season the food with hot and fragrant condiments. Food thus cooked gave off the most tempting and mouth-watering odours.

The absence of water-toilet sewage disposals, made the 'outhouse' an essential accoutrement to living in Bain Town. Like everything else, these varied in elegance as to the characters and desires of their users. Some were no more than a hole in the ground with a shack covering it. Others again were well-built, elegant and decorated. Let it be stated with emphasis that the people who inhabited Bain Town took a pride in their surroundings and their 'outhouses' were sometimes objects to be admired. An elegant one, according to the size of the family, was well built, camouflaged, and equipped for multiple usages. There was a seat, of comfortable height, with two or three holes cut in it to fit the necessary anatomy of the adults. On another wall was another seat with smaller holes to satisfy the needs of the children. This made waiting in a case of emergency unnecessary, and many a family conference was held in these while nature took its course. The course of nature has on occasion been reversed. It wasn't easy to exclude from these premises such poachers as lizards, 'bull frogs', cockroaches and other such crawling things. The occasional mouse and even rat was known to find its way in. It was rather disconcerting, when one was enjoying the long-awaited action, to feel strange movements on one's bare anatomy when you stopped to consider that this part of the anatomy was exposed to the searching antennae of cockroaches. The fearful mind brings about a cessation of the peristalsis. This has caused many a child to remain 'bound' for days.

There was a small wooden box attached to the wall in easy reach of any seat, which contained the latest Bellas Hess, Sears-Roebuck, and Montgomery Ward catalogues. These served a twofold purpose: on a lonely vigil leafing through one of these ogling all the pretty, unattainable American goods one whiled away the time. Secondly, since we did not know of the invention of toilet tissue, the softer pages of these large books substituted for this lack of knowledge most adequately. With sparing use, their hugeness added to their lasting until the new issues were received. The colourful backs of these, and other pictures that might be attainable, created some fascinating murals and many a rustic artist exhibited his works on these walls.

There was no fixed light for night excursions. To make use of them at night it was necessary to carry a lantern for which a hook was provided. As the 'house' was situated as far back in the yard as possible, night visits were not prolonged. The fear of 'sperrits', darkness and frogs hastened the action.

One consideration in the construction of a good 'outhouse' was the provision for an easy access to the pit. This was provided by a close-fitting removable back that facilitated the work of the 'night mechanic'.

It mattered not whether it was a hole in the ground with a shack over it or a sophisticated, decorated place, an outhouse had its own peculiar odour and it was not perfumed.

Mingle the odours of fresh baking bread, round and sweet with the pungent odours emanating from highly seasoned pots and the smoke from burning pigeon plum wood, and many, many 'outhouses' then you will begin to have some idea of what I mean when I refer to the odour of home – Bain Town.

Lest one gets the idea that Bain Town was a plush suburb, let me hasten to say that it was more like a rural village than a plush suburb. Nevertheless, it wasn't exactly a village, but a section of a small city, which, for most of the period covered by this writing, possessed none of the attributes of a big city. The majority of the dwelling houses of the settlement were no more than humble cottages. Many of them roofed with thatch and I do remember some that had dirt floors, but in my memory they were distinctive, sterile, clean and pleasant. All of nothing is good, and I would be misleading if I were not to record that there were those that were ugly, smelly and dirty. Most of these, however, were in the back alleys, and the N'ongas of Meadow Street were always quick to shun them, and to warn us that they were the homes of Congos.

The dwelling house of the average N'onga of Bain Town was a joy to the family who occupied it. Most of them were far from being pretentious, but each was kept in a way that spoke of the pride that these people had in that which they called home. Each one was substantially built and more often than not by the owner with the aid of his friends. There was a saying among the people of Bain Town: 'Never catch ya bird 'til ya cage is built'. So a proper young man, before he got married, built himself a home.

Each house had a verandah – or as we called it – a porch. If the ground was large enough, this went on two sides of the house, and I have known some that had porches on three sides. Sitting on the porch to watch the world go by was the favourite pastime of many families.

On the average a house would contain a bedroom for the parents, one or two for the children, a dining room and living room, which was called the 'parlour' or 'the front room'. Occasionally, there was an extra room in some of the affluent houses that served various functions.

Houses were used chiefly at night, for sleeping and for shelter. Daytime was spent in the kitchen, on the porch or in the yard. Visitors (if strangers or V.I.P.'s) only, were entertained in the 'front room', which was, at most times, off limits to the children. Only upon those occasions when they were to be exhibited to visitors were children called into the parlour; and then it was only for that moment. Once they had done the polite things, children knew to absent themselves from the 'front room', and repair to the freedom of the outside . . . Reflections on these days fill me with a certain nostalgia, for I still remember the simple beauty of the inside of these houses, especially those of the less affluent.

Cluttered as they were with bric-à-brac of all sorts, they were clean and neat. Wooden floors, showing wear from frequent and vigorous scouring with 'turbot skin' and octagon soap, were covered here and there with straw mats. Sidings, mostly unsealed, were papered with the colourful backs of catalogues, and other colourful pictures.

Cleveland W. Eneas

2 | Poetry

Sex

First you hear it
whispered about,
then you're told
it's forbidden,
Father stumbles
in his attempt;
anxious mother
hardly mentions it:
'Mind,' says she,
'no dirty tricks.'
By that time
it's too late:
you're already educated
from the streets,
by the boys.

Parents freeze,
teachers frown,
preachers denounce
but friends grin:
just as soon as
one little word
is bandied about.
Little word — heavy scene!
A sinister deed
according to some;
a celebration
for many others.
One small word —
(simply complex) —
yet pregnant
with consequences.

Don Major

Barefoot Boy

Little barefoot boy, a-wandering through the street,
Know you what in this life you seek,
What the day holds, who and what you'd meet,
Little barefoot boy
A-wandering through the street?

Your skinny arms, crooked toes and bare feet
Would touch the quick of hardy men
And make them want to weep; and yet
The world walks by, pretends it does not see
You in your rags and tatters
A-wandering through the street.

Little barefoot boy, where is your pa today?
He had drunk the last of Standard rum, and
They have taken him away. You hear no more
The drunken roar, the curse upon his lips.
Yet even in his drunken state, of love
        You had a sip.

Little barefoot boy, why no school today?
Is it a holiday that you wander in this way?
Do you dream of bright toys, other little boys
As you wander on your lonesome way,
You with your seven tender years
        Little barefoot boy?

Ah! do you see a door unlatched
And think it only a prank, child's play
When you enter and a handbag take away.
No one saw or did not care to ask you why;
So you cracked conch and bread did buy.
        Your first try?

Little barefoot boy, your hands are cold.
Wandering you've grown sullen, old,
Your heart turned stone! that was once pure gold,
A heap of stories to be told, your day-dreams
But, no one listens
        Little barefoot boy?

You know so many cuss words (by the score):
You have heard them so many times before.
When did you last laugh, little barefoot boy?
What makes you laugh at all, the hunger,
The empty in your belly, or
The forgotten unlatched door?

Did we not see your pleading eyes?
Did we pass you by somehow?
No matter — you sit silent in the courtroom now
In your rags and tatters, head bowed,
Little, skinny, unloved, frightened
> Barefoot Boy.

> *J.L. Mayson*

An Untitled Long Poem

Preface

A

I know I remember
But the memories come
Like a flood
Too quick for me
To depict each minute detail
But I know I remember
Being somewhere
Else
A long time ago
Not as I am now
Different I know
But how so
I cannot say
I know
But I cannot define it
Yet I was there
Floating
Drifting
Alive
Yet not human
But a being
Waiting to be made

B   It was a dark
And senseless world
Knowing you are
Yet feeling you are not
My world was vast and grey
With a billion little
Twinkling lights
Kaleidoscopic miniscule neons
Generating a power
From itself
Always changing
Into something else
Then
At times
Another force
Would create changes
That opened a warp
Forcing billions of us to escape
How many million eons
I spent there
I do not know
It was not like the other world
Where time IS
And life passes
Here time passes
We remain

C   Then the time came
When I was taken in
By that warp
And ejected into another world
Twice as hot and liquid
With billions of other
Little living things
Alien to me
Savage hostile parasites
In fear my kind
Rushed forward
Onward upward
And into
Winding caverns and grottos
Past caves and crevices
And mountainous peaks

Swept on by volcanic
Substances
Then suddenly I was
Alone
But still rushing somewhere
I saw a thing ahead
Shaped like an egg
I discovered I had a tail now
I whipped it to steer clear
But I could not
I crashed into it
And
I think I died

D   I remember awakening
In yet another world
And being something else
But I think I had been here
Before
Each day I become more aware
Of myself and my world
Of time and space
And feelings
And dependence
A foreboding premonition
Of being prepared for
Something
Of being more than what I know
Myself to be
And greater than
I ever was.

Phylmos Anthony Hall

Realisation

             WE ARE...
             MY BROTHERS AND I
             THE MOST HELPLESS OF INVALIDS
             THE MOST HANDICAPPED OF CRIPPLES
OUR ARMS HANG HEAVY FROM HARD WORK
AND USELESS USE
HAVING FORGOT HOW TO CARESS AND EMBRACE
OUR EYES SEE NO NEW SIGHTS
OUR SIGHT HUNGERS FOR NEW VISIONS
             WE FIND NO REST IN SLEEP
             NO COMFORT IN LEISURE
             NO PEACE IN THOUGHT
             OUR SENTENCE IS TIME
             AND TIME IS DEATH
             THE SLOW DRIP OF YEARS THAT
             DRAINS THE FLOW
             OF LIFE
             FROM OUR LIVINGNESS
             LEAVING THE HEART THIRSTY
             THE MIND BARREN
             THE SOUL VOID
EXISTENCE DIVIDED BETWEEN DUSKS AND DAWNS
MULTIPLIED BY DAYS AND MONTHS AND YEARS
THAT PAY THE COST OF YESTERDAY'S DEEDS
WITH HIGH INTERESTS OF BROKEN HEARTS AND HOMES
             AND LIVES
             AND IN THE VAGUE GLIMMER OF TOMORROW
             WE MAKE OUR PLANS
             BUT THE SOCIAL ECHO
             REVERBERATES...
             YESTERDAY... YESTERDAY
AND THEN THE DAY OF RELEASE COMES
WE LEAVE THE WOMB OF THIS IMMURE PLACE
DEPARTING BUT NOT FREE
             WE WALK ABOUT IN THAT NEW
             AND LARGER CELL
             WITH ITS HUMAN WALLS
             AND LIVING BARS
             LIKE OCCUPYING SOLDIERS
             'IN A TERRIBLY HOSTILE AND ALIEN COUNTRY'
             WHICH IS EXACTLY WHAT AND WHERE WE ARE.

                                        Phylmos Anthony Hall

Lament for a Li'l Old Lady

Naw I wan' yer ter sit an' lissen yer hear
'Cus I can' explain mersef too clear
An I wan' yer ter kno' erry word is der trute
Mer heart an' mer conscience clear

I ee say a never do no 'rong
I ee say a wuz always rite
But fer me ter survive dis long in life
Erry step a der way wuz a fight

An' ter bring up mer chirren . . . a had ten yer kno'
But only seven alive terday
I ee had no husban' ter depen' on
Jes me an' Jesus 'long der way

An' I ee had no job ter say go ter
jes plaitin' straw wid mer hand
An' wat a could hussle an' beg fer
I never had much hep from no man

I kno' wat yer tinkin' young woman . . . ah Lord
I kno' how yer feel mer dear
But lemme explain massef chile
Lawd yer kno' di life ee fair

Yer tinkin' naw say I mussee had plenty hep
'Cus mer chirren las' name ee alike
Yeah tis dif'rent pa fer seven a dem
Naw a kno' dat ee sound too rite

Try put yersef in my place dem days
I didn't kno' way ter fin' piece a bread
Den a man com' say ee wan' take care a me
An a did need som'place ter lay mer head

An' bein' a woman I couldn't fend fer mersef
An' der feller wuz so good an' nice
So a let 'im hav' ee way wid me
Wen he promise ter make me ee wife

55

Dat wuz der fus time . . . tell yer der trute
I didn't kno mer head from mer tail
An' even wen a start swellin' up like so
I still tawt baby is com' on der mail

Den he leave me rite dere wid nottin'
Not a soul ter say 'here' wid dey han'
An' pragnan' like dat a couldn't do much
It wuz a blessin' wen a meet dis odder man

He wuz li'l better . . . tell yer der trute
He really take care a me good
An' wen mer chile born he even ge 'im he name
So I stick by 'im like a should

But after a while he leave me too
An' ee left me heavy rite down
So I plait me straw an' sell li'l tings
Decidin' te stay on mer own

But in goin' tru' life . . . no matter who yer is
Yer wasn't made ter stay alone
An' wey a don' had couple chirren
I did need a man in der home

So it gone on and on but a always did mer best
Ter be decent an' live a Christan life
But I only meet men wat is make promise
An' never dem wa' is do rite

Chile yer could tink wat yer like 'bout me
Only Gawd kno's wat I bin tru'
I can' see ha I make it dis far no how
But I still holdin' on here wid you

Mer chirren don' grow up . . . dey all finish school
Off der money I make plaitin' straw
But as soon as dey get on dey feet mer dear
I don't never see dem no more

An' a still gatte pay mer rent yer kno'
An' buy li'l tings fer massef
So I really need dem few pennies
Ter hep me tru dese years wat lef

Naw like yer say first ... wen a did jes reach
'bout I ee never did nottin' fer der nation
Yer say a waste up mer life wen a wuz young
Den com' runnin' lookin' fer pension

Chile you wouldn't kno' ... ee nottin' I could do
So gimmee a chance yr hear
'Cus I ee gat nottin' a tall madam
Look like nobody jes' don' care

Wat yer say 'bout mer age? ... well a don't ritely kno'
But erry one could see mer needs
I feel mos' a hundred ... chile don't laugh
All wat a sayin' is real

Chile why yer frownin' up at me like dat
Is yer gon' turn yer back on me
Wat yer handin' me here? ... oh tanks ... dis der check
Naw I could get MY mudder som'tin ter eat.

Phylmos Anthony Hall

Twisted Logic

You never once looked around
to see what was really going down
you had it made.
but all the time you spent fooling round
with your outta town school girl clowns
you shoulda prayed.

You used to burn like a chimney stack
weed and pills they were you jack
God it's hard when you discover that
you wasn't really where it's at.

You were so amused
at the lectures about drug abuse
now when the pusher calls you can't refuse
now you have nothing, nothing left to lose
but your life.

You were such a liberated chick
we loved your weird, your freaky tricks
now you're cheating death for kicks.

*   *   *   *   *

Nothing's changed,
we're still deranged
now our poison is stored on the shelves.
            though everyone's forgiving,
we're still scared of living
            and will never escape from ourselves.

K. Andre Turnquist

Crystal Clear Confusion

encounter in the darkness
a discarded 8-track tape tried to strangle me.
the telephone, irritatingly composed in its tranquility
        stares at me
his hollow eyes
        glare at me.
until
metallic ringing rips the exposed nerves
as the shattered silence cascades all around.
panic at this intrusion
caressing the cold plastic of his leering face
then
wrong number — alien asking for another.
breaking down at this betrayal,
attacking my surrogate messiah
revolted at his writhing coils
as he lies bleeding on the floor.
alone another night
now that the phone is dead and gone
no calls
no hope.

K. Andre Turnquist

Strands

I guess I just aint gat no head for weavin
Dough de cotton tree and me
Live very near each odder.
NO, PAPA! DONT YA KILL DAT SPIDER:
MAYBE IT CAN SHOW TA ME
A TING OR TWO BOUT SPIRALS AN SYMMETRY.

Dis web of life I been weaving fer some time
Just aint been spirallin right;
I just cant seem to get all dem distant strands
To pass back tru de centre —
I probly aint start dem off right in de first place.
NO, PAPA! DONT YA KILL DAT SPIDER:
MAYBE IT CAN SHOW TA ME
WHAT DIS LIFE OF MINE BEEN HIDIN FROM ME,
HOW YA GET SPIRALS AN SYMMETRY
OUT A 300 YEARS A SLAVIN HISTORY,
300 YEARS A WORKIN ROUND DE COTTON TREE.

Now watch me spread my literary presence.
Watch me prove the uselessness
Of this shift away from Bahamian dialect.
Watch me crawl between the lines of immediacy and distance.
Perhaps by losing the thread
(If it's not already lost)
I can show you what my poem means.

See? I have already spun myself out
Across the strands of my own weaving;
I have become entangled in the web
Of my lines of jerky parallel
And convenient repetition.
But I have failed to demonstrate
Either with native or foreign grace
The nature of the spiral, the grace of symmetry.
But don't you dare equate my failure
With a momentary lack of aptitude:
The lack, you see, is permanent.
And do not think my limitation is self-imposed:
I am most adequate when I perceive most clearly
The fact of my confinement.

Remember my attachment to the cotton tree
And know that I am prone to be strung-out
Across the myriad strands of my own weaving.
NO, PAPA, DONT YA KILL DAT SPIDER!
LET ME WATCH TILL I AM RECONCILED
TO THREE GODDAMNED HUNDRED YEARS OF SLAVIN ON
    MY ASS
BY A SPIRALLIN, SYMMETRICAL, BAHAMIAN COTTON
    TREE.
Or, failing that, let me contrive
At least this esoteric vindication.

Melvin B. Rahming

Black Resurgence

He is here now
But he will come tomorrow —
A new-new breed of cat,
Big brilliant and black!

Crashing through the walls of his misunderstood traditions,
He will come.
Pulling himself from the seeming quicksand of his myths
To the solid rock of his reality,
He will come.

Down from the cross of cultural oblivion
Unto the long and sometimes perilous road
That leads him to himself
Up from the grave of a secondary existence
Into the sunlight of his primary blackness
He will come.

Researching, exploring, and deploring
The grandeur, foibles, and crucifiction of his past,
Accepting the tension-filled struggles of his present,
Moving toward the salvation of his future,
He will come.

Yanking from his neck the breath-quenching yoke of Christianity,
Recognising the resultant scars left on his consciousness,
Retaining from that religion-for-slaves
Only those aspects which seem innate and true to human form.
He will bear, for example, the weight of his own cross,
Follow himself through his own living deaths and resurrections,
Rely on the prick of his own nature's spur.

He is here now,
But he will form himself tomorrow —
A collective brotherhood of black experience and intelligence
Furthering the process of black rediscovery;
Millions of feet kicking holes in the ground
Until deracination is no more;
Millions of soles hardened and numbed
By hundreds of years of walking on hard times.

He is here now, but he will speak tomorrow —
A new language — direct, potent and compelling.
He will speak with a new voice,
A new confidence,
A new maturity;
And the sound of his voice will echo eternally
Within the halls of consciousness of the earth;
And his message will be charged with credible logic
And incredible truth.

He is here now,
But he will wait until tomorrow to show his many-thousand faces —
Arresting, firm, awesome and magnetic.
His look will cut through to the marrow of things.
Weak men will flinch under his perceptive stare;
Strong men will glory in the greater strength seen in his eyes;
But all men will be the better for having seen him.

He will be strong —
Millions of hands reaching out for contact with those who embrace
The struggle to epitomize the best in humanity —
His hands will shake the very foundations of society,
Only to make that society, paradoxically, more solid;
And through him his society will be forced to reckon
Not only with its blackness, but also with its universality.

He is here now,
But he will come tomorrow —
A new-new breed of cat,
Big, brilliant and black!

Melvin B. Rahming

Mailboat to Hell

Lord, help the mailboat to Hell.
Lord, help the mailboat to Hell.

The mailboat to Hell is filled to the cabin
With souls crying words they don't know
Such heavenly cries as Freedom and Justice
And curses for John Statusquo
Ah, but this cut is muddy Lord
This cut is rough
This sea is deep Lord
Are words enough?

I'm trapped on the deck of a ship doomed to sink
If the captain don't trust the crew
I'm caught in a swell of the crowd that won't think
But depends on the skill of the few
Oh, but the sea is muddy Lord
How trapped I feel
The cut is so dark Lord
And who's at the wheel?

Patrick Rahming

Power

Power
Power
Power to the people
Power to the priest
Power to the politician
Power to the poor
Power to the powerful

Masses 'a screamin' ignorance
racin' like a bat out 'a hell
inta hist'ry
vot'n
ta exacise they God-giv'n right
vot'n
to make they contribution
vot'n
to hep the Guv'mint lick
them trech'rous Opposition boys
who wan' ruin the country
vot'n
fuh the man 'a they choice
the man they never see b'fore
vot'n
ta hep bring down the cruption
an' the fav'ritism
vot'n
ta try and get in
on the Jags an' the night clubs
vot'n
cuz vot'n
is the only power the people gat
'cept vot'n ain' much power
if somebody else guh choose
the choice

    Power
   (HO-HO-HO)
     to the people

Patrick Rahming

Breakfast Bruise

I was sitt'n down the other day
Tryin' t'get some food
And the waitress she was a ogly thing
Feelin' in a ogly mood
She was cussin' left and cussin' right
Insultin' erry one
Swearin' on the Bible
An' braggin' bout her son.
She was servin' slow as snail
Ain' nut'n she serve was done
I couldn't resit temptation
A axin' what was wrong.

She say, 'Wha' hap'm?
You ain' never wake up feelin' tired eh?

I got seb'm chirrun
In muh house tuh feed
A man what does drink
An a daughter what does breed
M' insurance due
Since week b'fore las'
I ain' talkin bout rent
An' muh stove outa gas
Ain' nut'n wrong
What money can't fix
But t'ings so tough . . .
An' black people don't tip.

Apart from that I fine.'

Patrick Rahming

Stranded

From
anvil boots
to ungrown beard
and
finely-carved
stippled ebony
'fro
past
Joseph's multi-coloured
Terylene shirt
the rhythm
oozes
to his nerve-generators

he likes
his funk
served hot
with butter
and a little conch
quietly going mad
with Quincy Jones
or making love
under
Grover Washington

closed eyes
cool
semi-detached
anxiety
going nowhere
by Concorde
lost in
trying to take off
in flair-bottomed
vertical
frustration.

Patrick Rahming

Still and Maybe More: a Trilogy

Saturday
afternoon fights
with/over broken rum bottles
still leave
gaping wounds
and little black children
crying
still think Santa Claus
is white
after two years

To grow
civilised men
feed
upon the foresight/hindsight
of artists
who have the right
to paint
      sing
          tell
the truth as it hurts
               them
Politicians, materialists
and other anarchists
have the right
to silence
artists

Study the thought
and wonder
      about the sameness
Study the past
and wonder
      about change
Study
   to find
      the difference.

The image
of Bain Town/Grassroots
which sat boisterously
drinking
in a hundred bars named Briteley's
or eating boiled grouper
served by
(perhaps) the last, fierce
big-bubbied Nango woman
has climbed the hill
and descended
and seeped under the door
like the smell of boiling guava
into the Houses of Parliament
where boiled crab and dough
is now served
           under glass.
It looks the same
two years after
the fireworks
it looks
           smells
                    tastes
like boiled fish and grits at Kentucky Springs
like boiled crab and dough
at sunset
in Stanyard Creek
like okra soup
by the dock
in Rock Sound
it looks/smells/tastes the same
but changing

Two years of bleeding
Two years of searching the horizon
for friends
Two years of
more
           open palms under the table
more
           empty pockets on the streets
more
           advice from the United Nations

more
    dreams and schemes
    to become reality or fail
more
    chances to break away
    and leave
    or stay
more
    efforts by the knowers to be do-ers
more
    knowledge of the ignorance
    and the meaning
    of poverty
more
    pride in being
    whatever it is we are.

Birthdays
are meaningless
except to measure the process
of maturing.
Two years old
and growing.

Patrick Rahming

Political Farce

(Red Burrows — Polka Humes)
    3151074   3151086

Today
    Two brothers moved on
And the voice of the people
    claimed
Justice was done

Two souls for one!

    I wonder
Are the 'gods' satisfied?

Today
    Two brothers moved on
Used and discarded
    Like torn garments
Swept up in a mechanism —
    they probably
Never even understood —
That tries to justify·
    Legalised Murder
      with quotes from
    The Good Book
And a mask
    Called Justice

Dennis Knowles

Savacou

Savacou number five
Arrived in the mail today,
Shoving back to consciousness
Remembrances of what it used to be
Not long ago: those passionate days
When I first learned the art
Of being myself, or at least
What I thought I ought to be,
Angry and black,
Like other classmates,
Other artists, learning to be black,
And learning anger.

In that high time
I thought we had a choice,
We, the choice descendants
Of some African tribes
Flourishing once,
Now presumed dead.
Complacently I saw myself
Guiding multitudes by my art,
As each who practiced art at UC
Saw himself,
each with his multitude.

Fired with enthusiasm, we separated
One, almost two years ago.
Keen, somewhat hallucinated,
Each came home, each
With his own ambition, and
The crisp white paper
Anticlimatically awarded
Six months later
Meant very little
To most of us
And perhaps nothing
To the rest of us.

The mission was something intangible
But burning: that we
Though shattered by distances
By sea, by differences
Of national policy
Could bridge the gaps
Turn the tide,
Renew
In this new world
Ancient acquaintances,
And together
Revive the tribal dances,
Feeling the wind rush free
On cheek, the lusty fire
Of freedom, the warm
Brotherhood of blackness
Loose limbs, the dampness
Of dew in the tall bush,
The tingle of the lion's roar
And the softness of slumber
In the wide wild wilderness.

Two years ago
We had a choice, we felt,
We, the choice descendants
Of the old world. We'd be
Together once again,
Experiencing as it used to be ...

Today, with Savacou's arrival
That dream is poignant,
And I wonder what became
Of those other dreamers
Who scattered to sow
Their stardust to the winds
Down south:

I cannot imagine them like me
Frustrated, and somehow defeated
In my art, somehow reckless now
Of that previous ambition.

And strangely
It matters little
If people read
Or heed
These intermittent seeds
Of dust and ruin;
Whether there's any understanding.

All is a blank road
And mirages have faded,
Or if they were not mirages
Then eighteen months
Have shot their solidarity to pieces.

There is no way ... There is
No way back to the tribal dances,
No way ... no way back to the ancient
Ritual, the past's romanticism.
Quietly I wonder, has the world's cynicism
Stained them too? and if so
Do they think still
Of the old ambition
Or is it covered
By two years' dust and mildew
As mine? we felt
We had a choice then
As Savacou reminds.

Time is an endless pendulum
That swings in one direction only,
As its weight moves everything . . .

Ideals especially.

Robert Johnson

Back to the Root

Confounded with new business:
This is all my energy;
Dollars and cents, the office rent
And money for payroll bothers me.
I try for the root, the dark shoot
snaking down to the foot of my brain
where all I want to do remains.

It is simple to say I am trapped,
A dancing racoon snagged by the feet,
By Commerce in an iron clamp;
It is easy to hope –no, to know– that someday
Comes the scamper of running free . . .
Free to get to the root of things
To get to the root of me.

A surge of young poets, they say,
The flowering of art, the birth of creation;
Our minds are now blossoming, spring is the thing
As we witness the birth of the nation.
The racoon in me claws to the root of things,
To the scamper of running free:
Freedom to get to the root of things
To get to the root of me.

Stark is the picture that we must outline,
Bare as the shell on the sand,
White as bleached coral, coconut hard,
Black as the back of my hand.
We must get down to the root of things,

To the root of the bread-fruit tree:
Writers must get down to the root of things
To define nationality.

Robert Johnson

Sun in my Skin

There is sun in my skin:
I do not have the graces
Of the rich and cultivated.
Cutlery confuses me
And when I go to banquets
The food don't agree with me.

But in my brash vibrating arm
The cowbell dances;
And when sun meets brother in my skin
Its fire enhances what I am:
Bahamian.

Robert Johnson

Walls and Neighbours

A fireplace, a patio,
Carpet and rug from this wall to the next
Are proper to a middle-class context.
I, black as I am, in a black man's ferment,
Question my incongruous discontent.

My neighbours do not know me ...
The rattle of my car, my friends,
Are needless to their sentiment.

My neighbours do not know me:
Their quiet has been startled
By my footprints in their garden.
Expatriate wee, I bring the seed
of my country's flowering
To the inmost sanctuary of this wall.

Carpet and rug, from this wall to the next,
Are proper to a middle-class context.

Not by deliberate mission
Did this dark invader come
To wedge his alien presence
In the fortress of their wall ...

For black and white
Is a checker game
And each eats other
To the end ...

The black intruder
Comes to share
Their peace and quiet;
In his wall
A door shall lock
When he commands:
His longing
Is the same
As their great longing
With a different name.

Donald tells me
That peace and quiet
Is a bourgeois game.

My neighbours do not know me . . .
Each wall is mutual protection
And each smile
Hides miles of separation
From their door to mine.

Robert Johnson

East Street

East Street beats
Staccato rhythms dumbly;
The heart of our city,
Our culture, croons a melody.
And I,
Her child,
Her offspring,
Feel
The tremor of a new
And long-awaited wakening.

I,
With my beaten mind,
My pain
From centuries of restless sleep,
See shackles melting
At my feet.

We of this land,
These sun-stroked islands,
Know the whip-clenched burning hand
Of slavery.
The tumbling sun and sea,
Cool wind and hurricane,
Are new to most, though loved for centuries:

For most of us
The bleeding root of our culture died
In Africa:
Our hearts and minds
Were tuned then
To sing another melody.
Jungles and mountains,
The river's sodden heat,
Tall bush and broad savannah
Have lost their meaning:

Our fathers' blood
Lies cold . . . cold:
Our sleeping minds
Lie cold.

But now,
As East Street beats
Its just-learned ancient melody,
We dream of sunrise in the east.

The city street is clogged;
Night grips,
And all around the sound of sleep
Intrudes its cunning tongue.

Robert Johnson

West Indian

I am a West Indian
for the raging love
I have
for the beach
and the sea
and the sweet smell
of the salt wind
and winding, windy sea.

I am West Indian too
for the taste of breadfruit
And the childhood of sapodilla
and seagrape and solime
And the sleepy house
of roaches
and rats
And fear in the night
and drums in the night
And the rustling thatch
in the roof
when dawn approaches.

Robert Johnson

Tainted Scene

The wind like a cutting edge
Pierced the skin of the poorly clothed body
Mixing fear with trembling
In the dark while the small town slept.
Tears, filled with anger and passion
Released the solitary irking of abuse;
Pinching cold searched deep
Surfacing the nagging shame,
The terrifying thought,

'My father, step-father, touched me
    Used my body, causing me pain
    Staining the bed . . . my life!'

Face, too painful to touch
The threatening brutality, she dare not tell
Fearing the consequences, more serious than blows
Her step-father's promised wrath
Mixed with expulsion from home
Community disgrace, torturing shame
Blood stain on the bed . . . her life.

Livingston Malcolm

In the Distance of my Mind

In the distance of my mind
I hear a slow rugged beat of drums,
I can see black bodies
Moving in time to that slow rugged beat
Lips that are cracked from heat
            of the sun.
But there is a feeling of satisfaction
For there is freedom and love.

In the distance of my mind
Life is uncertain and there is confusion.
I no longer hear the beat of drums
Nor do I see black bodies speaking
            to each other.
Something has happened,
There is a smell of death.
The white creatures again
Have taken another step.

In the distance of my mind
I hear slow solemn beat of drums,
I see black gloomy faces,
My brothers and sisters
Forcefully bound together with
Rope and chains.
Freedom is lost and
Love is turned to hate.

In the distance of my mind
I see laden ships headed for a new
            world
I see my black brothers toiling
In the heat of an unknown land.
Jumping at the crack of the whip.
They worked hard to reach the
            day's quota.
To work hard for the man
Is the only way to stay alive.

In the distance of my mind
I see my black brothers disgusted
          and tired,
I see them throwing down the
          hoe and machete,
Determined to fight for a better
          life.
I see, black men and women
Standing tall fighting for equal
Rights for their brothers and sisters.
For some, freedom is far away
For others where there is life there
          is hope.

In the distance of my mind
The white evil forces are
          pushed aside,
And my brothers and sisters are free.
Free to mould their own destiny.
A new day is dawning.
But the attitude of some black
          brothers
Are the only scars left behind by
          the white devil.
The situation is changed. My brothers
          have names.
And they are beginning to understand
          who they are.

In the distance of my mind
Everything seems to be so familiar,
I seem to be a part of this new
          scene.
Yet I am not sure I want to be a
          part of it.
One evil has replaced another,
Power and money have caused
My brothers not to trust each other.
Some realise another change
          must come.
But this time it must be a change
          of attitude.

In the distance of my mind
I can see a time I do not know.
I see proud black brothers and sisters
Aware of their past and they hope
        for the future.
There is no fear of crime and
        violence.
Living is for now and it must be
        good
That others might also have peace.
My brothers and sisters are free at last!
Praise God! Praise God! Praise God!

Livingston Malcolm

Economic Blister

Tensed days
Impressing
      Neglecting
Poor economy
The growing
      Debt.
Angry waves
The blaring
      Cry
  'The poor dissatisfied'
Want to know why
  The country's wealth
Running an uneven course
     'Neglecting me
      ... cheating you'.
Disguised ambition
The deep seated foundation
Seeks out
    The poor,
Believing in an unrealistic
     Hope,
    The trade union.

Strike,
Take your stand,
  'The poor dissatisfied'
Want to see now
  The country's wealth
Evenly distributed
Creating a week's work
      'Feeding me
        ... clothing you'.
Ruthless strikes
Economic blister
Country impeded by
  Homemade disaster:
      Crime and
        Violence giving vent
  'The poor dissatisfied'
Want to know when
The country's wealth
  Properly managed
Without government
      'Squeezing me
        ... mutilating you'.
Saturated crises
Running their course
  Unemployment ... inflation
The poor facing destitution.
  Theft ... rapes
Robbing society, leaving distaste.
Efforts of help
      Fading in despair
  'people dissatisfied'
Want to be released
... economic blister
  ... lingering abscess
Anxious days
Spreading neglect
  Spreading neglect
      'People dissatisfied'
The growing
      Debt.

Livingston Malcolm

Calypso Boy

Calypso boy, sing me a song,
Beat me a rhythm proud and strong.

Calypso boy, come play for me,
This calypso girl, a melody.

Calypso boy, take my hand
And walk with me through calypso land.

Calypso boy, you have the key
To a life that's good and a life that's free.

So, calypso boy, sing me a song,
Beat me a rhythm proud and strong.

Ava Adams

Now is Then

When is the alone time?
The countryside is bare, cleanstripped
and naked like the naked silver birch.
Lifeless, huddled leafless are the hopeless
hands, thin silver clenching. The frosting
on the windmoan birch is stilled
by ice which freezing simplifies in death
and is alone.

When is the alone time?
Pictures painted are old sunsets
Golden laughter pictures tinged with red deep red of song;
sunset paintings, dull crimson mixed with dusty gold. Rich
love like ruby wine but teased from amber laughter.
The merry touch of tingling fingers
tasting by prearranged mistake.
Champagne
and deep red lanterns loving in the amber bubble

of amber champagne laughter. Hopes and fears encircled
floating free through rainbow windows.
Soft bubbles whisper, while floating red and golden
kisses shower. Crimson rose confetti petals
tossed carelessly and borne
away on amber.

When is the alone time?
Sunset, sunrise. And the wine
is turned to blood. The bubbles burst
and only the wet, washed sky is silver
clear behind the chillclenched
birch.
Pictures changed to dreams are frozen
by the Thing released at dawn then separated
fear from hope,
till God has mesmerised the sunset
into unforgiving ice-forgiven night.
Now is the alone time
while the chill claw finger of the silver birch
is ice-forgiven to the night of life — and love.

Yes, until then now becomes a when,
this is the alone time.

Liam Nelson

My Heritage

My heritage is of the night
Of dry-thatch cottages
Of painted faces
And of dreams.

My memory shows strange, snowless
    winters,
Dry mountain tops,
Green fields and trees
That never grey or die.

So I stand misunderstood, with
My snowless winters and evergreens,
Hated for the thickness of my lips
And my memories of drums.

Basil Smith

Decked in White and Black

Decked in white
And black,
Adorned with red
And gold,
Lawman stands erect
On small striped
Box of black
And white.

In the shadow of
His blue umbrella
The sun
Cannot reach him.

Cars, buses, bikes and surreys
Hurry by,
Happy to have passed his hand,
But others must
Be stayed by his command.

Tourists pass in admiration,
Their snapshot-memory
Or questions small
Are no bother to him at all.

He's only there
In weather fair
At breakfast, lunch
And five.
Surely he's
The only lawman anywhere
That keeps a beat
So neat.

Edward A. Minnis

The March of the Hermit Crabs in the Rain

How wonderful,
yet how strange,
to see hermit crabs
marching in the rain.
For months they've lived
beneath the rocks
waiting for the sound
of those wondrous drops.
Then suddenly from under
their covers they proceed
with a hermit crab in a whelk shell
firmly in lead
and thousands more following.
Their destination no one can tell;
it seems they only want to get wet
and display their shells
that they found washed upon the shore
along with the seaweed and driftwood
which they simply ignore.
Though to some hermit crabs
finding a shell that fits isn't
always that easy in life;
sometimes one has to settle for
a perfume bottle cap or an old clay pipe.
But what does it matter?
To hermit crabs it's all the same —
they only want a chance to march
in the rain.

Ashley Saunders

Punky's Place

Herby an' Basil, Harcourt an' me,
Rudy an' Pete, if they can get free;
Langford an' Charlie play with us too,
Duffer comes in to make up the crew.
Friday's the night, Punky's the place,
Fo Bimini shooters once a week race.

Pool's not a game, to us it's an art:
Making one quarter last from the start.
Can't drink too much or you might lose your head,
For one of us waitin' to stand in your stead;
And Punky will laugh, to make more disgrace,
In Bimini shooters once a week race.

'Bout nine o'clock Punky brings in the fish:
Fry, boil or souse — just grab-up a dish.
Friendship gives flavour, laughter a sauce,
Queen Punky's presence, the best second course.
A challenger stands with a smile on his face,
For the night is still young in the once a week race.

That's how it was for week after week;
But now Punky's packin': home to Deep Creek;
And nine lonely shooters just wander the street:
'What shall we do now, where do we meet?'
The bar's just a bar-room — not Punky's Place,
And no one has heart for the once a week race.

Van and Gerry Oldham

Tools

The tools have always been here:
Before Columbus sailed, joining Old to New,
The Islands waited for their destiny.
The hands of Carib, Arawak, Lucaya
Left few marks on the land,
For the tools were dull —
The tempering incomplete.

Raw iron from Africa
Fired in the crucible of the Middle Passage.
Alchemy of Europe wrought to forge the steel,
That the tools might take an edge
To cut the barriers
Dividing men from men!

Only when these tools had quarried
The building blocks of Reason and Compassion
From the hard rock of Ignorance and Intolerance,
Barring the minds of many men,
Could true Freedom come —
The step from child-hood to Maturity!

Our people are the tools of State,
Shaping a Nation, not for today
And sweetness of passing pomp and show;
But that our children may say with pride:
'These Islands gave New Genesis to Man!'

No room then for doubt and fear:
The Tools will always be here!

Van and Gerry Oldham

Ode

In the midst of this snow and this silence
Is the place where it's hardest to be
When the heart is a tom-tom drumming
For an island across the sea.

For an island whose winter is gentle,
Whose temperatures never can freeze,
With the resident, Spring, masquerading
As scarlet leaves green on Fort Charlotte grape-trees.
With the resident, Spring, masquerading
As scarlet leaves green on Fort Charlotte grape-trees.

In my mind I see pictures of small streets
Where greetings come back without pause
And the smiles that I give to passersby
They return as a matter of course.

They return friendliness in like measure
Quality that for wealth can suffice.
Merely thinking of home brings a pleasure
Which surpasses in cost chilling frost and cold ice.
Merely thinking of home brings a pleasure
Which surpasses in cost chilling frost and cold ice.

Telcine Turner-Rolle

Encounter with a Chickcharney

At six o'clock one May morning
I was going to feed the sheep
When I came across a chickcharney
Awakening from sleep.

Chickcharney blinked his saucer eyes
Surprised to see me there
And I myself was so amazed
I stood stock-still with fear.

He had a queer and mixed-up form
Like none I'd ever seen.
His arms were bird, his ears were mouse,
His legs were in-between.

And when he spoke, as speak he did,
I marvelled much to know
He could not rise into his nest
Where he wanted to go.

Because he'd hurt his penguin wings
He asked me if I'd try
And lift him to his house of straw
Among the branches high.

Where two tall casuarinas crossed
Their limbs above the road
I gently laid Chickcharney down
And left him feeling good.

The folk who lived in Coakley Town
Would not believe me when
I told them of my morning walk
And my chickcharney friend

But early as I rose next day
And opened up the door
There glowed a pearl more wonderful
Than any seen before.

Telcine Turner-Rolle

Crossing the Creek

Point of land, small point
Far across the waters blue,
Choppy waves in between
Makes us wonder what to do.

Ferry-boat so small
For the journey o'er the creek,
Taking five weighty souls
When the weather looked so bleak.

But we risked, stepped in,
As we braved the horrid thought,
Clutching tight to our bags,
Or what trivials we had brought.

Winds were fierce, hard winds
Drove the salt sprays in our face,
Dried the water, left the salt,
Stiff and ashy every place.

Billows rolled, boat leapt,
Weight of bodies left the seat,
Boat fell, stomachs rose,
Churned and empty, sick and beat.

Land ahead seemed dim,
Spraying salt forbid the view,
Throbbing temples, praying hearts,
In each breast the tension grew.

Land at last, boat still.
Underneath a towering dock,
Not a step leading up
From the low and craggy rock.

Men like monkeys, scaled up,
Ladies, ah! must hoisted be,
Much embarrassed clutched their skirts,
Tough for ladies, you'll agree.

Then the four tramped the street,
Spied the school and made their way,
Puffed their chests and smoothed their hair,
Education men were they.

Susan J. Wallace

Bulla Claudy Funeral

Now Ole Ba Claudy son an' me
Was teachin' side by side,
So I coul'n' help but go ta Church
When Ole Ba Claudy died.

A only 'tend ta show ma face
Fa de family ta see,
Den sneak ma way unnoticed
To de side-door an' be free.

But de seats in Church start fillin' fas'
Each bench in dere had folk,
An' when four women block me in,
I'ne laugh, 'cause ain' no joke.

Den all at once, one blastin' soun'
O' trumpet fill de air,
An' when I turn ta look out,
Half de funeral was out dere.

Now how dem people t'ought ta fit
In a Church already pack,
Was beyond me; yet de drove kept on,
An' none was turnin' back.

An' las' ta squeeze dere way inside
Wid de body out ahead,
Was a host o' mournin people,
All dem family ta de dead.

Den start de hoopin' session in,
An' how dem women wail!
While de men jes' keep on singin'
Else de whole ting woulda fail.

One woman get de Holy Ghos'
In de middle o' my bench,
An' when she did done shake me up,
Ma funeral clothes was drench.

Dis must o' bin one Elder now
Who stan' an' take each card
Off erry single wreat' ta read,
An' boy, he could read bad!

De Pastor time! An' he stan' fort'
Wid sweaty, baldin' head,
Start callin' folks by rows ta get
Dey las' gaze on de dead.

An' 'fore I had de time ta tink
How bes' ta 'scape da plight,
One usher dere was beck'nin' me
Ta forward to ma right.

Fool me, I play like I didn' see,
But when he shout, 'Moo on!'
I step right up de aisle-way
To de side-door, an' was gone.

Susan J. Wallace

Ole Zeke

Ole Zekiel used ta call 'eeself de Mayor o' he lan',
He born dere, he grow dere, de folk he understan',
He was teacher,
He was preacher,
He settle law dispute.
He cure de sick,
Know erry trick,
Ole Zeke!

Zeke never leave his islan' home in all he forty year,
An' he didn' plan ta go no place since he bin livin' dere.
But he cousin,
Come a-buzzin',
From de Sout'ern U.S.A.,
An' coax da man
Ta seek his lan',
Ole Zeke!

Ole Zekiel start protestin' loud, he'en gwine no
      place, he say,
Dem boat ain' safe, dem plane was worse,
      why play wid deat' dat way;
He was happy,
An' a Pappy
Ta a family o' ten,
So 'ee stan' 'ee gran',
Talk up like man,
Ole Zeke!

He cousin prime 'ee slippery tongue ta start 'ee
      job on Zeke;
He call 'im ole, he call 'im green, he call
      'im frail an' weak.
What a teacher!
What a preacher!
A scared ole-fashioned man;
When dem islan' folk
Done hear da joke,
Po Zeke!

Ole Zekiel fix 'ee business up an' start a-packin' strong,
He tell de people he gwine leave, but he'en gwine
      stay too long.
Wid 'ee cousin
He gone buzzin'
To de Sout'ern U.S.A.,
But 'ee heart beat fas'
As de boat gone pas',
Po Zeke!

De people crowd de beach like san' ta tell Ole
      Zeke goodbye;
Some wave dey han', some shout 'ee name, some ole
      folks start ta cry;
But da teacher,
Da preacher,
Make 'em promise not ta fret,
'Cause de trip he take was fa all dey sake,
Say Zeke.

Den Zeke did soon done breedin' in da great big city air,
He'en reach dere good, he gone down town ta get
      'eeself in gear.
He did wearin'
Colours darin'
From 'ee foot rite to 'ee head,
'Cause he t'ought ta be
A man ta see,
Ole Zeke!

He take 'ee stan' beside one shop, in biggety
      mayor style,
Wid pipe in mout; an' walkin' cane he 'ten ta
      gaze awhile;
Den a rumblin'
An' a tumblin'
Start comin' from behin',
An' soon Zeke see
Dat was no place ta be,
Po Zeke!

Nor'wester win' couln' catch ole Zeke a-haulin'
      down de street,
One iron critter whole mile long bin close behin' 'ee
      feet.
It start hootin'
An' den tootin',
Zeke t'ought 'ee time did come,
So 'ee up one tree,
By jove! 'ee free!
Ole Zeke!

De nex' t'ing dat Ole Zekiel knew he plane was
      headin' back;
He moo so fas' ta catch da chance, he'en even had
      time ta pack.
On de double,
Duckin' trouble
Wa done turn 'ee whole head wite,
He back home ta stay
Till judgeman' day,
Ole Zeke!

Susan J. Wallace

Islan' Life

Man kill, try ta 'scape, head fa big city town,
Fine de middle, pitch rite in, ge' loss,
Take job, make frien', live 'ee life ta de en',
Not de Law, ony Conscience is 'ee boss.

Man kill, try ta 'scape, stay in lil islan' town,
Town so small, 'tain no place ta ge' loss,
Erry 'squita tell de tale, frien' ta frien' widout fail,
Now de Law, not ya Conscience is ya boss.

Das de trouble wid de folks in dese lil islan' town,
Errybody is ya cousin or in-law,
Take care hol' ya tongue, wedder ole or young,
Or ya show ta win' up in de lion jaw.

'Fore ya talk, clear de groun', know de people
    stannin' roun'
Don' mistake tell a cow head 'bout 'ee tail,
If ya love, love a while, make show she'en ya
    Auntie chile,
Or ya hackl'up chil'ren show ta tell de tale.

Erry time party time, same ole people mullin' roun',
Not a bloomin' odder new face ya could see,
Dey wear out de lates' news passin' on de same ole views
Waitin' till anudder happnin' come ta be.

Islan' life ain' no fun less ya treat errybody
Like ya brudder, ya sister, or ya frien',
Love ya neighbour, play ya part, jes' remember
    das de art,
For when ocean fence ya in, all is kin.

Susan J. Wallace

lion jaw = trouble
hackl'up chil'ren = deformed children

'Cause the Arawak is Angry

In the quiet,
In the evening,
In the Carib atmosphere
stands a boy all full of dreaming
And that boy has not a fear:

'cause his soul admits no yearning
'cause his soul is very free;
In the quiet of the evening
By the Caribbean sea.

In the quiet,
In the evening,
In the Carib atmosphere
sits a man all full of conflict;
And that man is full of fear:

'cause his soul admits a yearning
That his soul might be set free
In the quiet of the evening
By the Caribbean sea.

In the quiet,
In the evening,
In the Carib atmosphere
runs a man berserk in vengeance
lighting fires everywhere:

'cause the Arawak is angry,
That his people are not free
In the quiet of the evening
By the Caribbean sea.

Norris Carroll

When THE MAN Besieges Your Land

When THE MAN
Besieges your land
With the gun
You're lucky;
'Cause you
And your brothers
Could always run
And take up
The gun
In defence.

But when THE MAN
Besieges your land
With The Dollar
You aint gat no brothers and soon
    You aint gat no land
To holler about, either.

But there is one hope:
You can always . . .
Get on a boat
And sail
To South Africa.

Norris Carroll

Of 'The Barren'

From this Eden, my Paradise today,
I shall wander but never stray.
For here are the roots of the tree that will spread
Its branches far and wide. Not dead
Will I be, when rising from the sod
Are the many things that breathe of God
In various ways — the riches I know.
This land, with symbols through which I find
Blessings to share with all mankind.
This land which gives to me the birth
Of a being anew through my passage on earth.

Meta Davis Cumberbatch

Poem for Mothers

Strong women,
glueing together
families for absent fathers.
Surrogate dads,
who soothe and rear
your children while
your man absconds —
To yet another woman
to be left alone.
Bearing and rearing
his careless seed.
And yet,
our weakness and our pride
go hand in hand,
with anger —
to their beds.
And so it goes.
Lives fragmented with giving,
and being taken.

And so one night
Thursday, Saturday or whatever,
a sister kills or self destructs;
While huddled in our hopelessness,
I wait my turn.

Cheryl Albury

Superwife

Did you see her?
That damned
mouthing robot.
High on detergents, cleaners,
husband's socks
and children's knickers.
DID YOU SEE HER?
Damned programmed
idiot in a dolly's body.
Priming, preening, plastering
her brain and soul
with the virtues of giving.

DID YOU SEE HER,
my friend?
Today she was at her best.
(or worst, some say)
Today's the day
they strapped and carted her away.

Cheryl Albury

Welfare Baby

Brown bundle,
defenceless he lay there.
'Mother's only sixteen,
doesn't want him.'
'Besides she's not sure,
Was it Harold or Jim?'
'Nose is straight, hair is curly —
Surely it's a white man's baby.'
Brown bundle,
defenceless he lay there.
She reached out to hold him, but couldn't;
Her offering a silent commentary.
Brown bundle,
Defenceless he lay there
Unloved, Nameless
Too soon a casualty.

Cheryl Albury

They Tell a Story about a Farawayland

They tell a story about a Farawayland and
I learn to read about people in Farawayland
And to write about people in Farawayland
And to speak like people in Farawayland,
Its Faraway culture, its Faraway men
Because my thoughts, my spirit, my soul
Will not inhabit their Farawayland
But rather flee beyond where my people
Are clothing themselves to debut
On the naked stage of my native land.

Jerome J. Cartwright

102

Barnum's Animal Crackers

There, just where you would expect
to find them, on the white shelf
of a large general store
sitting modestly
among the newer brands, teasing
me back into childhood

Roughly two by six, identical
lettering, as colourful
as memory, and —
no less than a miracle —
a fragile white paper handle
with the smell of Saturday afternoon

I turn in the breezes
of an island settlement half-
listening to the local gossip
my own images of visits
to dark shacks and box-sized
shops redolent with age

Those who stayed behind
after fighting the stones of the old roads
have no doubt forgotten
Only I count the gestures
that betray the regularity
of the ebb and flow of the years

The brown seaweed with scattered
bits of broken bottle, the games
of hoopla and bingo to bring
in funds for the island band
a welcome to the weekly mailboat
as it wends its way
south to the Caribbean
have existed for more than decades

Indoor plumbing, wall-to-wall
carpeting, talk
of the breakdown of washing
machines, all these surfaces
fooled me for an instant
into patchwork vision

If I bought the box of crackers
blond animals
shaped by the same cutters
would march forth
to spread their sawdust magic
over taste-buds
grown dull with years

Marcella Taylor

Taste of Apocalypse

A huge seabird flies in silence
over the shore, across the shallower
waters. Faint green ripples barely cover
dark gardens of the gentled sea
The bird directs its beak
toward the dock, sets broad claws
on a table-top rock beside a paling

I make sandal imprints along the beach
Sand joins dark blocks of beehive rock
Almond leaves spread like the palm
of an open hand. I walk
the narrow bank of the canal
its low water floating
invisibly to meet the ocean

I cannot say that I could survive
in these sparsely-habited surfacings
of the sea's depth. The silence
is only half of it. Sadly,
it is the horizontals
that predominate, falsely
recording a world at rest

I make a note of intrusions,
one or two unrigged sailboats, naked spars
jutting above hilly shoulders. They are not
enough. Broad Norman church towers,
gradually sloping hills, ranch houses merging
with the landscape, dwarfed wooden
palings to keep the dock from flooding

Even a second bird, standing poised
in the water, craning a slender neck
to vainly simulate the giraffe
of the earth's dark interiors —
all add to a world beyond
apocalypse or one
unacquainted with that first sin

Those of us who walked beyond the gardens,
measure pleasure as the intermittent
cessation of pain, cannot lift
the broken conch shell but to name
in its faded exterior the casing
that will gnaw through to destroy
the pastel glow of its inner surface

Yet even aliens may press an ear
to the shell to listen for an instant
to the echo of primordial
waters, raise a mouth to touch its pointed
edges, breathe hard into a hollow interior
to bring to birth the clean music
of an untarnished universe, counterpoint
to the whistle
of the aged wind over the land

Marcella Taylor

3 ‖ Plays

Single Seven
by Susan J. Wallace

Characters	MAE a housewife
	EZRA ROLLE her husband
	MILLIE MAE'S friend and a divorcee
	LEILA EVANS a writer for the numbers racket
	CORPORAL RIGBY a policeman; one of
	LEILA'S customers
	INSPECTOR SMITH a policeman

ACT 1	**Scene 1**
	Time: Breakfast time
	Place: The ROLLE'S dining room

MAE *is busy in the dining room putting the last few things on the breakfast table before her husband EZRA comes in. She yells for him as he walks in fixing his necktie and clutching a Bible under his arm.*

MAE:	[*surprised*] Oh! How did you know so well I was ready?
EZRA:	The scent, dear. When I smell coffee and bacon together I know you're ready.
MAE:	Pretty good figuring. [*Pulling out a chair*] Let's get to it because you should be on your way quite soon.
EZRA:	That's the cry every morning, 'Hurry, it's almost time to go.' You sometimes make me feel that you're real anxious to get rid of me.
MAE:	[*leaning towards him*] You really think that? After all the things I do for you? The way I always stick by you in everything? [*Pouting*] a woman can't even want to see her own husband on time for work now.
EZRA:	O.K. Pookie, you know I was only kidding. [*Looks for a moment deep into her eyes*] Look, before this little play of ours goes too far and I have to leave for work

with you not speaking to me again today, let's read our daily scripture passage, all right?

MAE: If you say so.

EZRA: [*he opens his Bible*] The passage this morning comes from Matthew seven, beginning at verse seven: 'Ask and it shall be given you; seek and ye shall find; knock and it shall be opened unto you. Beware of false prophets which come to you in sheep's clothing, but inwardly they are ravening wolves.' You know, Mae, that first verse seems to stick in my mind; 'Ask and it shall be given . . . seek and ye shall find . . .'

MAE: [*beginning to eat*] That's an interesting verse, all right. That came from Matthew seven, verse seven? Nothing but sevens, hey?

EZRA: And you know, it's strange but another verse from that passage reminds me of the lesson I read in church yesterday: Beware of false prophets. God sure planned this little world of ours in advance. He knew from those days to warn us about wolves – crooks we call them today.

MAE: And lots of them are around too, boy. The biggest shots around here are crooks so I don't blame the struggling little man if he grabs all he can get . . . He never gets much, anyway.

EZRA: Mae! How could you say such a thing?

MAE: Well, it's true, so I might as well say it even though I have no intentions of doing it myself.

EZRA: You know better! And Mae, about this message. Even one of the hymns in church yesterday seemed to be warning us.

MAE: Which hymn was that?

EZRA: Number eight, I think.

MAE: What did it say?

EZRA: Something about resolving to know the Lord in all we think, speak or do.

MAE: I wouldn't crook anybody, but I always try to remember the parable where the man gave the talents to his three servants when he was leaving to go into a far country. You remember how the servant with the one talent went and buried his while the others with the two and five talents traded and doubled theirs? Well, I don't hope to bury any talent I get. I may only make a little money sewing for people who

EZRA: are always so anxious to have their clothes but never can find the money when it's time to pay, but I know one thing – I intend to trade whatever I get. Now what kind of trade can you do with the little money you make? Look honey, your Ez would be happy if his little Mae just kept on burying whatever talents she has so long as she can find them when she needs them, O.K.? I guess I'd better run before I'm really late. I'll brush my teeth and be off.

MAE: I was just about to remind you of the time.
[EZRA *goes out. The phone rings.* MAE, *startled, looks towards the door where* EZRA *has gone out before rushing to the phone.*]

MAE: [*quietly*] Hello! ... yes ... Millie? I thought it was you. You're early too, you know ... No man, not yet, he's just about ready to leave ... If you leave now he'll be gone by the time you get here. Um ... huh.

EZRA: [*off-stage*] Mae? Mae!

MAE: [*into the phone*] Look, I have to go. He's coming.

EZRA: [*re-entering the room*] Who was that?

MAE: Who was who?

EZRA: Who was that on the phone?

MAE: Oh, the phone ... um ... that was a wrong number. Some idiot wanted one Harold or other.

EZRA: Harold again, hey? You just wait for them to call for Harold again tomorrow morning; I'll fix them up. You just let me answer it ... Well, I'd better go now. Bye love. [*Kisses her and goes out.*]

MAE: Bye sweetheart! [*She looks after him a while then begins clearing the table before MILLIE arrives. She stops and talks to herself*] Well, what do you know! My Christian husband has sure been dealing in sevens this morning – Matthew seven, verse seven. These sevens sound real good to me. Besides that I can't remember the last day seven fell.
[*A knock is heard at the door and MILLIE walks in.*]

MAE: Hi, there! Girl, you nearly scared the daylights out of me this morning.

MILLIE: You mean because Ezra was home?

MAE: You aren't kidding! He wanted to know who it was on the phone and I gave him that Harold story again. I don't know what I would do if Ezra picked up that

phone as he says he's going to do. He said he's going to give that person an earful.

MILLIE: Don't worry. If he even answers, as soon as I hear his voice I would hang right up, same as I did the last time.

MAE: Make yourself comfortable while I clean this place.

MILLIE: So what's new?

MAE: Girl, the best bit of good news is how Ezra came right here this morning and gave me single seven.

MILLIE: What do you mean gave you single seven? Which Ezra are you talking about? Certainly not your Ezra, hey? No, no, it can't be him because the only thing he hasn't tried his hand at in church yet is preaching. So how do you mean he gave you single seven?

MAE: Well, he doesn't know he gave me the number, but he gave it to me all the same and when I'm finished hitting that today in White Dot House and in Cuba House, girl, we're going to be pretty well off. Do you know the little scripture passages I told you Ezra reads every morning? This morning it just so happened that it came from the seventh chapter and the seventh verse of Matthew, and that's bound to be single seven.

MILLIE: Sounds good, all right. What else came out of this little prayer meeting you all had this morning?

MAE: [*thinks*] Oh yes, he said the words 'Beware false prophets' kept sticking in his mind and that a hymn in church yesterday had the same kind of message too, but I haven't figured that out yet.

MILLIE: Did he say what hymn it was?

MAE: Yes, number eight. But I don't see what that has to do with single seven.

MILLIE: You don't, hey? Girl, when are you going to learn? You forgot that time I dreamt about eight, and seven fell in White Dot House in the morning and one fell in Dwarf House in the afternoon hey? Why, even I who only reached as far as grade six in school can figure out seven and one make eight.

MAE: But how are sensible people to know it isn't six and two, or five and three or even four and four? All of them make eight.

MILLIE: Look girl, how many times do I have to tell you that when you get a lead number you have to back it in

	every way possible? I make every combination I can think of then play the number backwards if it isn't a single number. If it is two numbers like twenty-five, I add them and call them seven, subtract them and call them three, multiply them for ten and even divide them if I can.
MAE:	Sounds like that's a lot of money to put down on one number.
MILLIE:	What's ten cents on a number? And if you make a catch for every ten cents you put down you get back six dollars. Don't forget that.
MAE:	That's true, hey? I don't understand all the time how you figure things out but I'd better stick with you for as often as you win!
MILLIE:	You'd be stupid if you don't because the one thing with me is that I can go into this thing all the way. I don't have no husband to be hiding nothing from or sharing nothing with. That was a blessed day when he decided to leave because I was just getting a little bit tired of having to share my winnings with someone who didn't help me to get them. Anyway, that's beside the point. Let me tell you what I dreamt last night.
MAE:	You dreamt, Millie? Everybody's dreaming.
MILLIE:	And it isn't any common dream either. It's coming to me right now as clear as day. I dreamt I was standing on the beach, all by myself, down in San Salvador . . .
MAE:	That's because you were born there . . .
MILLIE:	And it was night. And I could hear a buzzing sound starting and stopping. I looked all around but I didn't see anything. Then I thought to look up, and lo and behold! Up there in the sky were two patches of bright things looking like stars, but they were too big for stars, and besides that they were moving up and down the sky.
MAE:	Stop your lies!
MILLIE:	I swear it's true! But you haven't heard the good part about it. I counted those little bright objects one by one and I'm sure there were seven in each patch. Seven again, Mae.
MAE:	What good luck on a Monday morning! Ezra gave me sevens, and now you dreaming about sevens too.

	I'm going to play seven and seventy-seven!
MILLIE:	Wait now, let me finish. As I stood there gazing up I didn't hear the buzzing sound any more. Then a lot of noise started coming from the beach. Girl, I only looked down in time to get myself out of the way of a great big truck speeding down the beach right in my direction.
MAE:	Truck speeding in sand?
MILLIE:	You bet your sweet life it was. If you had seen the way that big machine was moving and coming right after me – I had no choice but to jump for my life.
MAE:	Did you catch the number on the licence plate?
MILLIE:	Didn't I tell you it was night? Hum ... I was so scared at that time I didn't even have the presence of mind to see who in the devil was driving the truck, let alone catch the number. Anyway, when I caught myself and looked around the beach was full of people – Cousin Maggie, Toompie, Daisy-Mae, Jeff; a beach full of black people.
MAE:	Oh my Father, that's bad luck right away. The King Tut Dream Book says that black people mean 'woe, sorrow, and grief' and the number the book gives for that is thirty-four.
MILLIE:	Don't be a fool, girl. Thirty-four could be three and four, and that's seven, remember? Now for those black people ... they could mean bad luck if we're stupid enough not to back up that seven. I'm up to every trick people could play, child.
MAE:	You need Joseph to interpret that dream.
MILLIE:	Well, I'm going to be Joseph today because we've got to get those numbers sorted out and head for that little back room behind Leila's Fruit Stand. We've got to make it before the crowd sets in.
MAE:	And I've got to hurry back to do some sewing and cook lunch for Ezra and let him meet his dear wife at home as usual – the innocent little housewife who could never figure out how to trade her talents.
MILLIE:	Stop your blabbering now and come let's put our heads together. [*She takes paper and pencil from her bag.*]
MAE:	Yes, they say two heads are better than one, even if one is a sheep head. Now look, I have a twenty dollar bill I made Saturday from Toompie's dress.

112

	I'm putting down the whole twenty dollars.
MILLIE:	You feel your oats today, hey? Gone up from two to twenty dollars.
MAE:	That's right. I'm putting fifteen dollars on single seven – that's a hundred and fifty pieces. Then, with that other five dollars, I'm going to back that seven. Let me see . . . two dollars on seventy-seven, one dollar on seventy . . . Remember that hymn Ezra talked about? Number eight? I'd better put one dollar on seventy-one too. That's nineteen dollars.
MILLIE:	And what about the thirty-four King Tut gave you?
MAE:	Put the last dollar on thirty-four.
MILLIE:	I think I'm going to buy those same numbers, but it won't be any twenty dollars. I'm playing the same three or four dollars as usual.
MAE:	You're going to be sorry. Don't say I didn't tell you so . . . Anyway, let's get cracking. Let me get my handbag. [*Goes out and returns with her handbag and compact.*]
MILLIE:	Eh, eh! Lipstick and all, eh? Father, when the cat goes out, rats take place all right!
MAE:	All set? [*They exit.*]

Curtain

Scene 2
Time: Late morning
Place: The back room behind LEILA'S Fruit Stand

LEILA enters examining a tally sheet on which she comments.

| LEILA: | I'd better try let that little child of mine hold on out there at the fruit stand till I'm finished tallying up these sales I've already made this morning. They say we're having hard times around here but this sheet doesn't look like anybody's experiencing hard times in Nassau. And my hand is itching too? That means money and it looks like it's going to be plenty too when I'm finished getting twenty-five per cent of all these sales. [*Sits at her desk and checks further*] Toompie . . . eighteen pieces of seven, ten pieces of twenty-seven, five pieces of seventy. Daisy-Mae . . . ten pieces of seventy-eight, four pieces of eighty-seven, three pieces of fifteen. Jeff . . . |

[*A knock is heard at the door. LEILA hustles the sheet into her dress pocket and busies herself tidying up the room. Another knock.*]

LEILA: Yes! Who's that?

[*A child's voice replies.*]

VOICE: It's me, Mamma. Mr Rolle bought two apples and he needs some change but there isn't any in the box, and he said he's in a hurry, and I can't leave the fruit stand, Ma'am.

LEILA: Which Rolle is it?

VOICE: Mr Ezra Rolle, Ma'am. He said he's got to get back to his job at the Telephone Company.

LEILA: How much change does he need?

VOICE: He gave me five dollars for two apples, Ma'am.

LEILA: All right, tell him to come in here where I'm cleaning this room. [*She busies herself cleaning, holding her back as if tired. A knock is heard at the door. She unlocks it.*] Come in, Mr Rolle. [*He enters*] How are you doing this morning?

EZRA: Can't complain. Could be worse . . . I ate so little breakfast this morning I got hungry so I sneaked off the job for a couple of apples.

LEILA: They're the best things for hunger. That's all I peck on myself when I'm hungry.

EZRA: [*handing her the five dollar note*] Your daughter said you'd give me the change from the two apples.

LEILA: [*taking note suspiciously*] Is there anything else you want?

EZRA: Oh no, just the apples, I . . .

LEILA: No, I don't mean like apples . . . Working people like you trade a little part of your earnings to make more . . .

EZRA: Trade? I don't think I ever have enough to trade. I'm the only one in my house with a steady salary, you see. My wife, Mae, makes very little from sewing and even with both of us saving nearly every penny we get, we can just barely make it.

LEILA: [*avoiding his gaze*] So Mae is a good saver, hey?

EZRA: She's quite a girl that Mae.

LEILA: Yes. As I was saying, I don't make much myself off that fruit stand but I take the little profit and trade it and with a little luck and the help of God, I can already afford a big station wagon even though I

	haven't learnt to drive yet. My house, even though it's clapboard, is already paid for, and now I'm saving to send my seven children to school. My husband who has a steady job can't make that kind of money.
EZRA:	That's interesting. How in the world did you do that?
LEILA:	I'll tell you a secret but I'm only telling you because you look like an honest, God-fearing man who could do with a little help. And from the time I first saw you, I liked you. [*Goes closer to him*] Have you ever heard of White Dot House?
EZRA:	White Dot House? You mean . . . ?
LEILA:	Yes, that's right. This House has a manager and plenty writers.
EZRA:	Writers?
LEILA:	These are the agents. People come in and invest small amounts of money on certain numbers every day. It's just like raffles they hold in the church. Whatever number get pulled out of the bag is the winning number and whoever bought that number gets six dollars for every piece he buys.
EZRA:	But that's gambling . . .
LEILA:	Plenty fools say that, but only poor people so fool. All you're doing is taking a chance with your own money, and if you think straight and keep your eyes open you can come up with the right number nearly every day.
EZRA:	I'm afraid, Miss Leila, that kind of thing isn't for me. I believe in God and whatever He has for me He'll give it to me whenever He thinks I should have it.
LEILA:	I agree with that. But I also realise that God has a-plenty of work to do and we have to help Him if we want to get ahead. That's why, me, before I buy my numbers every day, I listen to all that people dream the night before. Then I watch the numbers on the cars passing by this stand; I try to find out whose birthday it is and how old they are. Then I come up with a sensible number. And I usually warn my customers to do the same.
EZRA:	You're an agent? Sorry Miss, my conscience would never allow me. I don't want to get mixed up . . . or anybody belonging to me. That's police affairs.

LEILA:	O.K., I'll never try to force anybody to do what they don't want to do. But think about it and if you ever change your mind, let me know. Now, let me see . . . twenty-five cents each for two apples, so that's four dollars fifty in change. [*Counts the dollars*] One . . . two . . . three . . . four . . . Lord, what is this! You know, I don't have the fifty cents right now. Do you think you can pass back later for it?
EZRA:	O.K., I'll come back . . .
LEILA:	Look, I have a better idea. Why don't you let me put that fifty cents on twenty-seven for you?
EZRA:	Miss Leila . . .
LEILA:	No, wait, I'll make you a deal. If twenty-seven falls you can pick up the thirty dollars around three o'clock. If it doesn't fall you can pick up your fifty cents any time, O.K.?
EZRA:	I'll pick up the fifty cents later, Miss Leila.
LEILA:	O.K., Mr Rolle. Have a nice day now. See you later. [*He exits*] These preacher kind of people really can play hard to get. Talking about he doesn't want himself or anybody belonging to him mixed up! Ha! Wait till he finds out about Mae! . . . But I'll get him yet. I'll give him a little time to get rid of his pride. [*Sits and examines tally sheet. There is a knock at the door*] Who is it?
VOICE:	Millie and Mae.
LEILA:	[*opening door*] Well, the Bobbsey Twins, hey? How are you girls?
MILLIE:	You know me! I'm on top of the world all the time.
MAE:	I'm fine. How are you?
LEILA:	[*holding her back*] Child, my nerves are on me so bad this morning I don't know whether I'm going or coming. I don't know how to explain this. I boiled up some bush and drank it but nothing happened. I wouldn't be a bit surprised if I'm not pregnant again.
MAE:	How many would that make?
LEILA:	[*innocently*] Only eight.
MILLIE:	Only eight! Well, holy smokes! I had only one and I thought all hell had broken loose on my head. It's a good thing I managed to trade my little earnings and sent him to school in Jamaica when he was ten.
MAE:	It's very expensive these days giving children

116

	education. Ezra and I keep saying that if we adopt any children it wouldn't be more than two so we can give them the best.
LEILA:	When you trade your little earnings you're on the right track. Now anything exciting happened since yesterday?
MILLIE:	Mae decided on a whole bunch of sevens because Ezra read from Matthew seven, verse seven this morning and I dreamt about seven bright objects in the sky.
MAE:	But we're kind of worried about the whole lot of negroes Millie dreamt about. King Tut says they're bad luck.
LEILA:	Well, I dreamt the opposite of that last night. I dreamt I stepped flat-footed in a whole heap of . . . I can't tell you.
MAE:	[squirming] Ooh!
LEILA:	And girl, for all I rubbed my foot on the ground I couldn't get the scent off. I had to throw away the whole shoe.
MILLIE:	That's good luck, all right. What are you going to play today?
LEILA:	Well, in the dream book, they say that stuff means three, thirty and thirty-three and it means good luck too. But the book also says that whoever dreams about it must play their own age.
MILLIE:	How old are you?
LEILA:	Forty-three last May. So I'm not taking any chances. I'm hitting the forty-three, the four plus three – that's seven – and every number that has seven in it, expecially seventy-seven and twenty-seven. I think I'm going to play those threes tomorrow.
MAE:	Yes, because I think it'll either be single seven or seventy-seven fall today.
LEILA:	Sounds like seventy-seven or twenty-seven to me. You see, seventy-seven could mean two sevens.
MILLIE:	I don't really agree with that twenty-seven. I don't think I'm going to waste any money on that.
MAE:	Me neither. That'll only cost me more money. I don't think it will fall anyway.
LEILA:	Looks like you two already decided what you're going to buy so just give me your list I'll enter it on my tally sheet.

MILLIE:	[*handing over piece of paper and money*] The top set of figures are Mae's, the ones at the bottom are mine.
LEILA:	[*surprised*] Twenty dollars? Big money all right, and single seven are popular too! You two must know more than you're telling me.
MAE:	Of course not!
MILLIE:	From where?
LEILA:	All right then. You two can call around two o'clock to hear what fell. You know my phone number and the kind of question to ask.
MILLIE:	Don't worry. With all that money Mae put down on single seven I think we're going to be coming back. [*They leave and LEILA follows them to the door then goes back to her tally sheet and gloats over the money already there.*]
LEILA:	My twenty-five per cent of this amount will sure look good in my hand. If I'm really pregnant that baby and I could lie up in hospital like a queen. [*There is a knock at the door; the tally sheet disappears into LEILA'S pocket. She hesitates then goes to the door.*] Who's that? [*There is no audible answer. She opens the door and jumps on seeing the police uniform. She tries to close the door but the policeman pulls at it.*]
RIGBY:	Wait, Miss, could you please tell me where Miss Toompie lives?
LEILA:	[*recognising his voice*] Oh, Miss Toompie ... God, Rigby man, you almost scared the life out of me. For heavens sake don't do that to me any more. I'm not used to you coming here this early.
RIGBY:	[*loudly*] Yes, I'm looking for Miss Toompie. [*Under his breath*] Anyone in there with you?
LEILA:	No, come on in quickly before someone spots your uniform. How is it that you're on beat already? I'm used to seeing you after ten o'clock. [*RIGBY looks around sheepishly and LEILA continues*] Have you got some good hot numbers? [*He wanders around the room looking in at all the doors, still saying nothing.*] Looks like today is seven day! How does that sound to you? [*RIGBY slips a folded paper from the inside pocket of his tunic and hands it to her. She holds it for a while searching*

his eyes before opening it to read. Then slowly opening the paper she reads with terror in her eyes.]

Blessed Father! What is this! Tomorrow? Three o'clock?

RIGBY: And I'm supposed to be leading Inspector Smith here. So you see why I'm here so early.

LEILA: Why did they pick to do this? Do you think they found out you come here too?

RIGBY: I don't know. But for God's sake clear up your tallying and paying off as soon as you can this afternoon; warn all your customers today not to come in or try to buy from you tomorrow. And get rid of every trace of anything in this room or at the fruit stand that would give you away. Understand?

LEILA: Understand.

RIGBY: [*fidgety*] I've got to get out of here. If Inspector Smith ever dreams I'm anywhere near here I'll be pounding the beat for the rest of my life. [*He rushes to the door, lingers to look at LEILA and then adds in a whisper*] Take care! And remember, don't panic . . . play it cool!

Scene 3
Time: Early afternoon
Place: Room behind LEILA'S Fruit Stand

LEILA sits with tally sheet counting out money for winners and placing it beside the name of each winner. The telephone rings and she goes to answer it.

LEILA: Hello! Yes, this is Leila . . . who? Jeff? Say how many words in the telegram? Twenty-seven my dear . . . that's right. I don't know how that happened . . . There are plenty more like you. Listen, looks like it's going to be real tough tomorrow . . . that's right, JUDGEMENT'S COMING at three o'clock. Stay the hell clear because I won't be knowing a soul tomorrow do you hear? Don't forget now, and tell your friends. [*Goes back to her desk talking to herself*] Many of them will be shocked today when they hear twenty-seven fell. It's a good thing I played every number I could think of with seven in it. [*She goes back to her tally sheet and just settles in when the phone rings again.*] Hello? Yes, this is Leila ... Who? Daisy-Mae? Say how many days I'm going to be in Miami? Twenty-seven child. That sound like a hell of a number of days all right. I don't know why I pick that kind of time. Listen, looks like it's going to be real trouble tomorrow. That's right ... uniforms are involved ... stay clear and spread the news ... bye, now. [*Goes back to her desk talking to herself*] Nobody will be able to tell those people they didn't take that seven and seventy-seven out of the bag just because there was so much money put down on them. I wouldn't disbelieve it myself if that isn't what really happened. Some people are really crooked! I'm glad I'm not like them.

[*A timid knock at the door. LEILA listens, unsure*]
That's a knock? Or am I hearing things?
[*The knock is repeated*]
That's somebody, all right. I'm not taking any chances. [*LEILA hides the money then shouts*] Who's that?

EZRA: Mr Rolle, Miss Leila.

[*She smiles then goes to open the door.*]

LEILA: Hey, come in. [*He enters and she closes the door behind him*]

EZRA: I came to pick up the ...

LEILA: I knew you were going to be lucky. You just look like the lucky type. Even with the upset today you still won thirty dollars.

EZRA: Now Miss Leila, I didn't ...

LEILA: Oh, you don't have to apologise. Most of the Christians who come here are just like you when they first start. You should have seen one pastor when he first started. I almost had to break his arm. Now, he is my best customer.

EZRA: Miss Leila, I'm in a hurry ... if you'd give me the fifty ...

LEILA: Yes, I guess I'd better get right down to business because I don't have much time myself. By the way, no number pulling tomorrow but it's starting up again on the following day, O.K.? [*She counts off three ten-dollar notes and hands them to EZRA. He hesitates to take them. A knock at the door. EZRA snatches the money, pushes it into his pocket and starts,*

	terrified. *LEILA pauses for a minute to think.*] Look, you'd better hide yourself here in this bathroom. [*She rushes him in*] I'll give you the signal when it is safe. [*She glances around to see if all is in order, pushes the tally sheet in the drawer and the money in her under-skirt.*] Who's that?
MAE:	It's Millie and me. [*There is a slight pause then LEILA opens the door*]
LEILA:	[*flustered*] come in quickly and let me lock this door, child, because [*Whispering*] they plan to raid this place tomorrow and I'm not taking my chances.
MILLIE:	[*fairly loudly*] What raid?
LEILA:	Shhh. Shh ... You know it can't be insect raid, hey? I'm planning to get rid of the people from around here as soon as possible today because before sundown I want to clear everything out of here that even looks like it might be related to numbers.
MAE:	[*quietly*] You mean police ...?
LEILA:	Exactly so, so don't stand around asking questions.
MILLIE:	What fell?
MAE:	Yes, we'd better hurry and straighten that out.
LEILA:	[*avoiding MAE'S gaze*] Well ... er ... I don't know what happened but twenty-seven fell. I swear something must have gone wrong because I had most of my money on single seven and only a little bit on the other numbers to back it.
MILLIE:	You backed it with twenty-seven?
LEILA:	[*guiltily*] Yes, a couple of pieces ... don't you remember I told you I was going to do that?
MILLIE:	Who you told? You're a liar, Leila. You didn't say a word like that.
LEILA:	Well, look how this woman came here calling me a liar right to my face! Now woman, don't make my blood rise because I told you right here in this room that I liked twenty-seven and seventy-seven too. You, Millie, you were the one who told me you didn't agree with that and you weren't wasting any money on it. And Mae, you were agreeing with her. [*Turning to MAE*] Isn't that how it went, Mae?
MAE:	I .... I ...
LEILA:	Ain't no, 'I ... I ...'
MILLIE	[*to LEILA*] I thought you were hiding something.
LEILA:	[*rushing at MILLIE*] You wretched little ...

121

[*There is a knock at the door. Everyone stands still and looks at each other.*]

LEILA: Yes? [*There is no answer. Louder*] Yes? Who's that?

SMITH: Open up, police!

LEILA: Blessed God!

[*There is chaos inside with LEILA, MILLIE and MAE running in all directions. LEILA grabs up all the money and the tally sheet and stands for a second looking around for a place to get rid of them. She spots the bathroom and dashes for it. MILLIE and MAE are frightened by the police attempts to break down the door.*]

MILLIE: [*regaining a little of her cool*] Look, Mae, catch yourself! Sit down in this chair and the two of us will pretend we're just talking about those dresses that you made for me and they were too tight.

MAE: Y-e-es. All right! You mean the green and the . . . [*Another big bang on the door.*] Oh my God, what is this I'm in?

MILLIE: Keep talking about the dress, I say!

MAE: You said it's the green one and that . . . that . . . [*Confused*] Oh, I can't remember no foolishness this kind of time!

[*LEILA re-enters. MILLIE and MAE rise to meet her.*]

MILLIE: What did you do?

LEILA: Tore up every blasted dollar and flushed them out!

MAE: [*amazed*] All that money?

MILLIE: Hush your stupid mouth!

[*Another crash and Inspector SMITH and Corporal RIGBY walk in. RIGBY looks at LEILA sheepishly and tries to explain the early raid with his eyes.*]

SMITH: Who is Mrs Leila Evans?

LEILA: That's me right here. And who gave you permission to come breaking down this door that I paid all that money for? Just because you are a policeman you think you have licence to destroy poor people who are struggling hard for a living, hey? Let me go see what damage he did to this door.

[*She tries to go to the door to examine it. Inspector SMITH reaches for her shoulder to stop her.*]

SMITH: Just a minute, Mrs Evans. [*Shows his card and search warrant.*] I'm Inspector Smith and this is my warrant to search this place.

LEILA: Now why do you think you want to search my

	place? Here I am in my own little place minding my own business, and you coming here . . .
MILLIE:	[*clearing her throat*] Um . . . um . . . Excuse me, Miss Leila, but I think I must be leaving now because I have to go shopping before the food store closes.
MAE:	Me too. You see me here listening to other people's business? You'd think I don't have to go to cook my husband's dinner. Look, we could talk about those dresses I'm making for you tomorrow, O.K.?
SMITH:	Hold on you two! I may need to ask you some questions too.
MAE:	Who, me?
MILLIE:	What for?
SMITH:	[*to LEILA*] I'm afraid we're going to have to search your place.
LEILA:	What are you searching for? If you tell me and it's here, I could give it to you.
SMITH:	Evidence of illegal dealing in lottery.
LEILA:	What's that?
SMITH:	[*deliberately*] The numbers racket!
LEILA:	And why does this evidence have to be in my small little place?
SMITH:	We don't have time for any more questions, Mrs Evans. Rigby, search everywhere – shelves, desk drawers, cupboards, bathroom – everywhere!
	[*RIGBY scampers off, examining shelves, desk drawers, etc., then goes into the bathroom. A sudden cry of one startled comes from the bathroom then there is silence. Re-enter RIGBY.*]
SMITH:	What was that noise you made?
RIGBY:	Noise? Oh, the curtain blew across my neck as I searched and frightened me so I jumped to defend myself and catch the culprit.
SMITH:	Curtain? Are you sure it was a curtain? . . . I think I'd better take a look myself.
	[*He goes in and shortly the bathroom door flies open. SMITH comes out pushing EZRA and holding him with his arms behind him. MAE and MILLIE start in shock.*]
MILLIE:	So this is where he comes. Well! Well! Well! Even the saints are doing this! Ugh! Ugh! And scripture verses in the morning galore!
	[*EZRA makes for MILLIE.*]

EZRA:	You dirty little . . .
SMITH:	Take it easy, you! [*Turning to RIGBY*] Corporal, this man was in the bathroom hiding behind the toilet. [*Extending his hand with some money in it*] He had these four dollars in his wallet and these three crushed ten dollars in his pants pocket.
EZRA:	Look, Inspector, I can explain it all . . .
MILLIE:	He'd better be able to explain it. [*Pointing to MAE*] This lady here, Inspector, is his wife.
EZRA:	Believe me, Mae, this is all so silly . . .
MAE:	It doesn't look silly to me, Ezra.
EZRA:	I mean . . . I'm innocent, Mae. I came to pick up the change from my apples . . .
MAE:	The fruit stand is outside.
EZRA:	[*sternly*] Look, are you going to believe me or not? Besides that, what are you doing here?
MAE:	You know, if you had asked me that this morning I would have felt inclined to answer but not after this.
SMITH:	[*holding out the money to EZRA*] Look, you, I'm still waiting for you to explain this.
EZRA:	Look, man, I'm a lay reader in Church.
SMITH:	I believe you. It's those lay readers who run the biggest rackets in this town. Now, your name?
EZRA:	Ezra Rolle.
SMITH:	Job?
EZRA:	Technician with the Telephone Company.
SMITH:	What were you doing in that bathroom?
EZRA:	I came here earlier to buy two apples at the fruit stand and I had to come back here later to get my fifty cents change because Miss Leila didn't have the change then.
SMITH:	Did you get the fifty cents?
EZRA:	Yes . . . [*Looks at change in SMITH'S hand*] I mean, not yet, Sir.
SMITH:	And why do you have these three ten-dollar notes in a separate pocket and all crushed up?
EZRA:	I . . . I . . . [*Frustrated, turns to LEILA*] I told you not to . . . [*Breaks off on meeting LEILA'S gaze.*]
SMITH:	Do what, young man? Go on!
EZRA:	[*embarrassed*] She took my fifty cents and bought number twenty-seven. I told her not to do it. I distinctly told her . . .
LEILA:	Mr Rolle, you are a Christian, you know. You mean

	you could look me straight in the eye and say I bought a number for you.
EZRA:	Sorry, Miss Leila, but I can't lie . . .
LEILA:	You hear that? Say he sorry. [*To EZRA*] Well, it's no use saying you're sorry when you've already done the damage . . .
SMITH:	All right, we can continue the questioning at the station. I'll have another look in that bathroom before we all go to the station. [*He goes in. Individuals exchange glances. SMITH re-enters with two or three pieces of dollar notes on a piece of toilet paper. He holds them out to LEILA*] And you, Madam, must also be prepared to explain why you use dollar notes for toilet paper. [*Sarcastically after LEILA cuts her eyes*] Sorry we didn't have time to warn you of the change of time. [*RIGBY and LEILA look astounded.*] Come on, all of you. [*Pointing to MAE and MILLIE*] You as well. Let's go. [*They all walk slowly towards the door. As MAE passes her husband she pauses and whispers to him*]
MAE:	Beware of false prophets.
	Curtain

The Potato Dreamer

by Percival A. Miller

Characters   DANNY The Dreamer, a half mute
SAM KNOWLES His father
MRS RACHAEL KNOWLES Sam's mother, aged
MISS MYRTLE The seer
MRS ALSAIDA COX Rose's mother
ROSE The object of dreams
BILL DEAN Rose's betrothed
DREAMFOLD A woman/a man of Myrtle's conjuring
MAN In Scenes 1, 2 and 7 (Danny as he would wish to be)
WOMAN In Scene 2 (Rose as Danny presumes her to be)

ACT 1   **Scene 1**

A dingy, very modestly furnished little bedroom. There may be a window at right. Very soft dreamy music is being played in the background as the scene opens. A figure in a small bed, clad in a singlet and wearing what appears to be large trunks, is sleeping with his back to the audience. He is not snoring but clutches a pillow to him; his knees are drawn up, the bed appears uncomfortable for the man's size and height. A few articles of clothing hang over a straight wooden chair next to the bed. They belong to the sleeper.

Another man, somewhat ethereal in dress and manner, is pacing the stage slowly, thoughtfully. He is deep in thought; he crosses from right to left, then stops centre stage facing audience. He gestures, shouts:

MAN: Every man dreams of love!
A prince, a pauper, a fool,
[*Slower*]
The prisoner staring at the morning
through bars of steel
The King, combing his hair at the mirror
The schoolgirl, happy in her innocence
The sailor watching a port come into sight
The drunkard drooling where Night finds him
The housewife, elbow deep in her domestic labours
The old maid, sighing at a favourite photograph
[*The figure on the bed stirs.*]
Even an idiot, in a lucid moment, dreams.

126

That he can love, that he can be a King.
[*Shouts again*]
O my love, my love, her memories before me,
As every pleasant thing I ever knew!
[*Begins to dance*]
We have been writing letters
We have been writing letters
Letters will get us nowhere [*Stops*]
[*Thoughtfully*] So she says.
[*The figure stirs, turns.*]
I cannot write my thoughts, I said
Thoughts that keep whirling inside my head
[*Louder*]
I can but dream my thoughts I said.
[*One or two women's voices, off-stage.*]

VOICES: Danny I love you, I love you Danny.
[*MAN gestures toward the voices. The figure in the bed sits up, suddenly looks around, settles back to sleep, smiling and hugging pillow.*]

MAN: There they go, making believe.
[*Shakes his head*]
Life is funny
Life is ha-ha
Life is strange
Love is strange and sweet
Sweeter than an endless dream. [*Moves*]
[*Figure settles into pillow.*]

MAN: [*laughs*] Ha-ha-ha. [*Arms akimbo, laughs again. Does a kind of waltz of his own making, to the rhythm of his words*]
When I was a boy in Cat Island
I loved a sweet daughter called Rosie
Ta, ta, ta/ta, ta, ta/ta, ta
I kissed her by the well
I kissed her by the well
(I almost fell in the well)
[*Stops, grins*]
You could expect that. First time I ever kissed a girl like that, ooh!
When she put on her red dress
My heart wasn't worth a penny
I longed to see her sun-up 'til sundown
(All I wanted was the form I loved)

[*Dances again*]
O Rosie, Rosie, Rosie by the well
Who was it that kissed you
Only me can tell.
[*Stops, a bit downstage*]
She didn't love me then.
Said I ain't sound.
I wonder where she is, now.
Let her go! I don't care.
[*Shouts*]
I don't care
[*Softly*]
I am nothing
I am nothing
I shall be nothing
[*The figure behind him rises, slams pillow, face down.*]

MAN: There *is* nothing.
[*Gesticulates, speaks rapidly*]
When she says she doesn't love me all it means is that she cannot learn to love me. There's too much difference between us.
[*Slowly increases in volume so that by the end he is shouting*]
I am not the man for her and though I love her so that my soul would drown itself in Galliot cut or hang itself from a tamarind tree for her sake, yet she could not love me, and if the right man came along, nothing can help me, not all my love, for I am nothing and thus I will have loved her in vain!
[*Figure in bed kicks at the bedstead.*]

MAN: [*Tears off coat etc., throws them to the ground*]
I am nothing! I am me! A fool! I can't sing, I have no way to win her love.

A CLEAR VOICE
FROM AUDIENCE: God will help you.

MAN: God? I perceive there is none. If there was, why would he let us love what cannot possibly be ours. Why doesn't he heal me? Why doesn't he heal you? There is no one, you hear, No one!
[*Lights change . . . . Figure stirs. A woman in a housecoat enters from left walking hurriedly but as if in a dream.*]

WOMAN: O the child of my womb. O the child of my womb.

	[*Turns to figure in bed*] I am so sorry, honey, I didn't know. I couldn't help you being born. My child! [*Turns, exits right, wiping her eyes on her sleeve.*]
MAN:	[*picking up articles thrown to ground*] I have to take care of *me*. [*Another man enters from left, older, more brutal, walks toward the figure in bed. He is dressed in working clothes. Stops, tense, by bed. His voice is coarse, harsh.*]
SAM:	Well, for cryin' out loud. Look at this big, stupid boy sleeping here, as long as I was calling him to go to the field! I bet I . . . [*Grabs bed, shakes it, shouting*] Danny! Danny! [*While he does this, the MAN front stage goes farther right, as if to exit. His movement toward the right approximates the shaking of the bed. The figure on the bed does not rise. SAM grabs at the pictures of women above the bed, ripping them down.*]
SAM:	You good-for-nothing dummy, stay there sleeping till I get back with some cold water. [*He dashes off, left. The first man is nearly off-stage at right, an older woman, grey haired, enters slowly. She sees the figure in the bed, goes over to him. She sees the torn pictures over the bed, tries to repair them by re-taping them.*]
MRS KNOWLES:	Poor thing! [*The pictures keep falling, or perhaps her hands are not too steady. She calls softly*] Danny! [*The first man moves further off at this.*]
MRS KNOWLES:	Danny, honey, wake up! [*The figure on the bed stirs, as first man exits. SAM enters abruptly at left carrying water in a pail. MRS KNOWLES walks towards SAM, intercepts him before he can reach the bed.*]
MRS KNOWLES:	[*sharply*] What you think you go do with that water? Ain't you see the boy sleeping?
SAM:	You move outta my way. This big, lazy boy shoulda been out in the field fo' daybreak, workin'. He ain't got sense for nothing else! He'll work, or I'll anchor him!
MRS KNOWLES:	Now, Sam, you know how hard that boy does work. Why you trying to make him turn hatred against you! Gimme this bucket, I tired o' you pushing that boy around. He already a man, you know! [*She grabs handle of bucket to wrest it away.*]

	Sam, I wouldn't treat a dumb animal the way you treat that boy! Give me that bucket!
SAM:	[*still struggling but as if torn between giving up and going ahead*] Look, woman, get out of my way, before I . . .
	[*He doesn't have a chance to complete his verbal threat or accomplish it in deed, for the sleeper, DANNY, in a single motion, jumps from the bed, and stands facing the man angrily. Neither of them had expected this, so they both stare, in shock; they have not seen him react so violently before. Standing, he is still a ridiculous figure in his overlarge trunks. SAM puts bucket down.*]
MRS KNOWLES:	[*moving towards DANNY, puts arm around him affectionately*] Danny, child put on your clothes and come get some breakfast so you can go in the field with your daddy. He waiting on you.
DANNY:	[*pointing to bucket*] Ugh! Uh! Why uh glod wat?
MRS KNOWLES:	That's okay.
SAM:	[*in a terrifying voice*] And move your dumb self with life, before I knock you senseless!
	[*DANNY stands there clenching his fists. SAM moves toward him. MRS KNOWLES moves between them.*]
MRS KNOWLES:	[*gently*] Come, Danny. [*She steers him by the arm toward the right. DANNY picks up a couple of articles of clothing from the chair and goes meekly with her. SAM is shivering with rage.*]
SAM:	When I reach that field, let me meet you there!
	[*He shouts after the retreating forms of DANNY and MRS KNOWLES. Though his threat is pregnant with violence, we sense that he is more bombastic than intolerant in this instance. However, he is definitely to be reckoned with. The lights go down on his imprecations.*]

Scene 2

A rocky field. This may be suggested by a suitable backdrop, and the presence of potted shrubs in the background. Centre and toward the back is a large tree or shrub. Enough for possible shade. Left stage is empty, except for a bench. It is clear these are two different environments; left stage represents the locale of DANNY'S dreams.

Enter the man, SAM, the boy DANNY, wearing field attire; straw hats to keep out the sun, string sandals. SAM carries a basket and machete, DANNY three or four sticks with handles, and smaller basket. DANNY is following.

130

SAM: [*looking around*] I wonder how come Carl and Jimmy ain't here yet. [*To DANNY*] Put the seed under the tree.

[*DANNY puts down basket, SAM sits by tree right stage side, facing audience. Relieves himself of basket. DANNY does same, sits upstage from him; but enough away to show that there is no warmth between them. SAM reaches toward DANNY who flinches, as if expecting a blow.*]

SAM: Gimme them sticks, lemme touch them up.

[*DANNY hands him the sticks. He pulls them out of DANNY'S hands roughly, examines them critically and begins to shape them with his machete. DANNY assumes an indifferent, hang-dog air . . . When SAM is done he stands up, looks east toward the sun, stretches, clears his throat and spits. A crow sails by, as if surveying his efforts. SAM chucks a stone after it.*]

SAM: Look at that good-for-nothing bird! [*Gestures*] Dig up every blasted seed if you don't shut the hole good.

[*He takes out a cloth apron, a pan. He pours seed into the pan, and using a dipper, puts some into the cloth apron's pockets. This done, he covers the pan with a cloth and selects a stick.*]

SAM: Danny, don't sit there! Get some seed in your pockets and let's get goin' . . . . [*He is watching DANNY intently as if expecting him to do wrong. DANNY, flustered, reaches for the seed.*]

SAM: [*raising voice.*] Now boy, don't let me have to do something here this morning. This ain't the first time you plant corn, you know. [*DANNY wonders what he is doing wrong.*] Don't put in your pocket while you sitting down! [*DANNY gets up puts a few handfuls of seed in left pocket, takes a stick.*]

SAM: Work on my right-hand side, so I can see what you doin', and knock your senses out when you do fool.

[*The two begin to plant, side by side. This consists mainly of stabbing the earth with the point of the stick, throwing two seeds into the hole at a time, then filling the hole and tamping it lightly with the sole of the foot. This requires practice to perfect, especially the throwing the seeds into the hole, but is quite easy. The men move across the stage, right to left, quickly planting several rows. When they reach the field's end, which does not extend into the area*]

131

with the bench, they turn and start planting in the opposite direction. They may also replenish their seed supply at necessary intervals. The older man, although planting with more expertise, is slower than DANNY, and it is obvious that DANNY has to slow down at intervals to let him catch him up. He does this by becoming deliberately slower when he moves out ahead. The man tires, slows so that the planting has become almost slow-motion pantomime. SAM stops, leans on stick; DANNY does the same.]

SAM: Danny, finish planting this row, then start back like you was doing. I going to catch a rest. [*As if to himself*] I should have never gone fishing night before last. And my back nagging me again. [*Looks left*] I wonder where them boys is, they ain't get there yet. [*Goes off, sits under large shrub or tree, removes apron, lies back. To DANNY*] Use this, while I resting. [*DANNY accepts apron, returns to work. DANNY likes to plant and is pleased by the opportunity to prove himself. There is almost a skip in his walk, as if he has to restrain his exuberance. By this time, all the back rows have been planted, and he is now moving along the centre to front rows. He actually begins humming, though his song hardly sounds human. As he plants, he becomes more reflective, we see at the far end right stage, two figures, a man and a woman, moving toward the bench. They are not aware of DANNY'S presence; neither does he look at them or in any way acknowledge their presence. However, DANNY does pause, leaning on his stick.*

The man at right halts the lady, produces a handkerchief, wipes bench. This done, he makes a sweeping gesture toward the bench. Both are dressed as if they have been somewhere, perhaps to a social function.]

The dialogue between MAN and WOMAN on the bench in this scene is obviously between ROSE (as DANNY thinks her to be) and DANNY (as he thinks himself to be or wishes to be - an alter ego).

Setting, etc. may define the unreality of the dialogue - i.e. figures grotesquely romantic, or music or clothing.

MAN: My Lady.
WOMAN: Oh! Thank you dear sir. You are most kind. [*She sits, he assumes space beside her.*]
MAN: You're not chilly, I hope.
WOMAN: Funny you should ask, seeing that you have my sweater. [*Coyly*] Are you going to let your sweetie

132

pie freeze? [*MAN puts sweater about her shoulders, she leans against him.*]

MAN: That reminds me. I'm kind o' hungry.

WOMAN: How very romantic.

MAN: You enjoy yourself tonight?

WOMAN: Yes. I don't need to ask you if you did.

MAN: Why shouldn't I? Your cousin only gets married once every three years.

WOMAN: [*struggling to hit him*] You're terrible, you know that? One of these days I am going to pinch . . . [*She pinches him*] . . . and pinch . . . [*Does so.*]

MAN: . . . your nose. [*Holds her nose, kisses her.*]

WOMAN: [*in faraway voice*] Help, strangulation! Pincher!

MAN: If you call like that, do you expect anyone will come?

WOMAN: You never know. Never know who might be in the bushes, waiting to rescue me from your . . . [*Playfully*] . . . ungrateful arms.

MAN: Well, perhaps he'll be someone bigger than I am so that I can spray OFF on him.

WOMAN: Aw, you're much bigger than that. Even your proboscis.

MAN: Rude little Rosie.

[*She leans against him again. His hands go over her face.*]

WOMAN: My face is alright. Where you have your hand are my eyes; they can open wide, and shut tight. Then there's my nose, a beautiful little nose. Then there's my ears, capable of hearing a lizard swallowing . . .

MAN: You don't say!

WOMAN: I say.

[*DANNY resumes poking with his stick. Couple sit up, apart, as if engrossed in their own thoughts. DANNY looks over to tree to see if his father is still resting, then goes to tree, sits, puts head on knees.*]

MAN: We . . . we have to do something, you know. About us.

WOMAN: Like what? What do you want to do?

MAN: So you love him. Where do I stand?

WOMAN: Bill? Oh . . . Danny, you're more like a friend to me . . . you know. I could never be serious about you . . .

MAN: Why? Because I can't speak too clearly? Because of

133

what I am? What they say I am? What you think I am?

WOMAN: Danny, please . . . I don't know. I can't answer those questions. Don't you understand? If things were different for us, for you . . .

MAN: Rosie, for crying out loud. Do you understand that I love you?

[*WOMAN does not answer.*]

MAN: Do you understand what I'm saying? I love you. You mean my whole life . . .

WOMAN: No, no Danny, I . . .

MAN: What would you have me do? Change? It ain't my fault, you know. I didn't make me. Don't you understand. I have loved you all my life. I have never loved anybody else, I have never wanted to. I thought you loved me. Didn't you say so?

WOMAN: Yes, but Danny, I . . . you don't understand. I do love you, too. Please don't be like that.

MAN: No! You made it up! All I am is a frog. An idiot. A potato dreamer. That's all I am. Say it! Say it so I can hear it and be done with it.

WOMAN: No, Danny. Please. Let me talk to you. I wouldn't love you if I saw you like that. You ain't no frog, no potato . . . what was that, Danny?

[*The MAN does not answer at once.*]

MAN: Yes, all I am is a potato dreamer. Go ahead, say it 'til you know what it means.

WOMAN: No, what does it mean? When you say it, it hurts me, as much as you.

MAN: Yes. Just being crass and dreaming the impossible. That's all I am doing.

WOMAN: [*taking his hand*] Don't you remember me? I'm Rosie. I am just an ordinary girl. I can't see everything the way you see it.

MAN: Okay, okay. Maybe I shouldn't even be talking to you, is that it?

WOMAN: Oh Danny, why must you go on like that. You're making me feel so down.

MAN: Sorry. I didn't mean to. I just thought we'd talk tonight since I didn't have a chance to see you for a while. I didn't mean it to turn out like this. Let's forget it, then, you know; talk about something else . . .

WOMAN:	Easy for you to say.
MAN:	I guess I was just, well, dreaming too much and seeing too little.
WOMAN:	No. I don't think so. I just didn't think of things that way. You were so kind to me. I guess I took too much for granted.
MAN:	No. I took too much for granted, too. I wish I could tell you.
WOMAN:	You still hungry?
	[*MAN does not answer*]
WOMAN:	Suit yourself, then. I'm having a candy. [*Produces candy from bag. There is a silence.*]
WOMAN:	What will we do?
MAN:	That's all up to you.
WOMAN:	Well, you're in this too; at least you could say something.
MAN:	Well, you see, who'll I want, if you don't care.
WOMAN:	I asked you about us. Okay. Why not let's run away, then. Then I could love you as much as you love me.
MAN:	Won't work.
WOMAN:	Then we could at least be cool tonight.
MAN:	And tomorrow I'd still be a potato dreamer.
WOMAN:	If that's what you want to be.
MAN:	I don't.
WOMAN:	Then be Danny then. Not the one you see. The one I see.
MAN:	What is the one you see.
WOMAN:	He is quite a guy. Quite.
MAN:	You could bring out the best in me.
WOMAN:	You are the best.
	[*They hold each other again, kiss.*]
MAN:	I . . . I wish I could offer you everything, my love.
WOMAN:	No one can offer us everything.
MAN:	I wish I were different.
WOMAN:	Anyone can wish. The two of us are here.
MAN:	I'll always love you.
WOMAN:	Nothing will happen; things will be the same.
	[*DANNY, under the tree, stirs.*]
WOMAN:	Danny, Oh Danny, I think I am falling in love with you. I really am.
MAN:	So am I. All over again.
	[*They embrace. The lights dim for a second, when they*

return, DANNY is on his feet, looking around in surprise.
SAM still snores heavily under the tree. The girl has gone;
but the MAN is at extreme right centre turned theatrically
away from the audience. DANNY, half scared, grabs for
some seed, and tiptoes hastily back to his work. He plants
rapidly the few remaining rows near the field's edge, or
front stage. When he begins the final upstage row and is at
far left stage, he pauses immobile over his stick.]

MAN: O, that I had the eloquence of poets that I could win
her with a kingdom of words.
Or that I had the likeness of an ancient god that I
could charm her with a chiselled fineness
Or that the treasures of a dozen empires were my
own
That all her wishes may be my pleasure . . .
That we were of a different time . . .
[*Pauses*]
But we are what we are.
Walkers against humanity's night
Out of step
Out of tune
Some are of the living, of the light
Others of the uninstructed dead
Damned and doomed
[*Shouts*]
Curse my discomfort, curse my pain
I am but a fool
It will pass
[*Softens*]
As an untimely rain
And the creek of my remembrance
Will be as a rain-calmed pond
Purely reflecting my unpresumptuous thoughts
[*Paces*]
Before my birth
Before our births
We were so marked by random fate
That she should be the soul of innocence
Desiring most an ordinary fate
That I should be a cripple
And that my only form provokes disgust and hate
[*Shouts*]
I do not want her sympathy!

[*Shouts upstage*]
I do not want your sympathy!
[*Turns to audience*]
I want your love.
[*Turns slightly away, gesticulates*]
What does it mean?
Unending pain?
They will not give me love
They cannot give me love
And if I love them, it will be in vain.
She is like the sun's rising to me and my shadow
before me when my soul rejoices . . .
What the hell
All is well
I can eat and sleep and remember
[*Softly*]
It is often too much to remember
[*Intones*]
The soft curve of her neck
The music of her voice
The shining beauty of her presence
What the hell
In my old age and dearth I shall smile and remember
well.
[*DANNY, at the stick, moves forward on the final row,
planting. He pauses about centre of the 'field' area of the
stage, begins poking at the ground in an absent-minded
way.*]

MAN: [*In right stage centre*]
Our man, [*Points to SAM under tree*] he is so
engrossed in his own life and living,
The old woman, bless her kind heart
She sees
The two fellows, his sons
They do not see
How we are all part of a cruel plot.
And we can never escape
O to make a man, to let him be
To let him feel, to understand it all
And yet to bind him in a cage he cannot see
That all his days he shall endure the thrall
Of yearning to be free.
[*Turns away*]

Or, shall I die?
If I die
I shall not know her love
Again
[*Faces audience again, speaking fast*]
But if I live
How shall it end
Shall I be pleasant with shadows
Sickly memories
[*Points to heaven*]
Shall deities above afford me only illusions
[*Shouts*]
Let me die then, Let me die
I should die than live with shadows, illusions.
[*DANNY stabs viciously at the ground. The MAN at right rips off his shirt, throws it to the ground, in a paroxysm of frustration and anger so he does with whatever articles of clothing or wear he can destroy. DANNY chucks seeds angrily into vicious holes his stick has dug. As DANNY is so engrossed in his work, the man, SAM, under the tree, awakes suddenly and sits up, wiping his face with his hand crudely.*

SAM watches DANNY for a moment then jumps to his feet and removing his belt roughly, sneaks up behind DANNY, who is still angrily pitching the seeds into the holes.]

SAM: [*bringing down belt across DANNY'S back repeatedly*]
You good-for-nothing worthless donkey! Why are you wasting the corn? Why are you wasting the corn! Why are you planting the corn like that!
[*Accentuates his words with blows.*]
[*As Danny cowers and tries to defend himself against SAM'S rage, MAN at right, as if shocked, jumps off stage into audience level, scrambles back confusedly onto stage, he exits very hastily at right.*]

SAM: You dog. I'm gonna make you plant every damn grain again!
[*Lights go down on SAM'S schizophrenic rage.*]

Scene 3

A living room at ROSIE'S house. While the room is modestly furnished as befits a farmer in the Out Islands there are a few furnishings which seem ambitious and would perhaps be more suitable in a more elegant setting. Colour and neatness, however, predominate.

MRS ALSAIDA COX, ROSIE'S mother, is seated at a side table at right; partially facing down stage. A large radio occupies the end of the table farthest from the audience. MRS COX is shelling peas into a large 'fanner'. The shells, she disposes of into a large paper bag sitting on the ground by her knees. She is listening to the radio. It is some time during the afternoon.

There is a knock, off left stage.

MRS COX:	Yes? Who is it? [*Turns down radio.*]
VOICE:	Dean here.
MRS COX:	Oh! [*She looks around the room hastily, removes bag of shells to a less conspicuous position, goes right to admit DEAN.*]
	[*MR DEAN enters, a little behind MRS COX, who offers him the sofa.*]
MRS COX:	Come right in, Mr Dean. Make yourself at home.
MR DEAN:	Thank you. Is everybody out . . . ? [*Stops as if he is not sure he should have asked. He has a self assured and educated air.*]
MRS COX:	[*with a little mischief*] That's right. All of 'em out. Just me one here . . . I just send Rosie out. She should be back in a little while . . . How is this weather treating you?
MR DEAN:	[*seating himself relaxedly on far left sofa*] Oh, it hot that's all. It doesn't bother me too much when there's a breeze. Don't let me interfere with what you're doing, though.
MRS COX:	I was just shelling some peas. [*Returns to seat by side table.*]
MR DEAN:	And how's the man with the flu? Jimmy?
MRS COX:	He coming around. I tell him – 'You goin' to school tomorrow if only you go!' Too much trying to set my nerves on fire.
MR DEAN:	Yes. [*Chuckles*] That one is a lively one.
MRS COX:	[*rising*] Let me get you something cool. You'd like a soda, ginger ale, a malt tonic? Something else?
MR DEAN:	A malt tonic would be fine, thank you, Mrs Cox. [*MRS COX exits, returns with essentials for the same, serves.*]

MRS COX:	[*resumes pea shelling, with a drink herself*] How is the school coming on?
MR DEAN:	Oh, we're coming along well, except for a few little things. With the season soon to start, I'm trying to put together a good volleyball team, though we don't have the court in good shape yet. I meant to ask if you or Mr Cox wouldn't have any objections to letting Josh practise one or two evenings after school for the next month or so, perhaps Tuesdays and Fridays.
MRS COX:	Well, I couldn't say right now, but when Lemuel comes, I'll see what he has to say.
MR DEAN:	That's alright, Mrs Cox. Guess I'd see you again before we start to practise, anyway.
MRS COX:	Josh and Marie behaving themselves, eh?
MR DEAN:	[*chuckles*] They're doing fine. I think they'll do pretty well in their exams if they keep it up.
MRS COX:	They'll do their work, once you give it to them, you don't worry about that. And Lemuel says the same thing.
MR DEAN:	That's very nice. Mrs Cox. If all the parents had the attitude of Mr Cox and yourself, we wouldn't have any problems.
MRS COX:	You can't mind some of these people, Mr Dean. You just have to do your best. I know them well . . . I been here all my life.
MR DEAN:	Mrs Cox, what I also wanted to ask you, and Mr Cox, is if you'd mind my recommending that Rose be appointed as one of my teachers for the primary classes. The Ministry has given me the go ahead to recommend someone to replace retired Mrs Newton; and I couldn't think of anyone better qualified for the position than Rose; in fact, she was the only person who meets the requirements. I know she's been out of school for a year or two, but perhaps you and I might persuade her; that is, if this is all right with you.
MRS COX:	This is . . . well . . . she was hoping to get into Teacher's Training next year, but . . . I guess we'll have to discuss this with her, as you said. She's not doing much right now, anyway.
MR DEAN:	It shouldn't interfere with her getting into college next year, at least there's no reason why it should.

	In fact, it might help her.
MRS COX:	Well, I really like to see young people get ahead. Especially mine. So many things happening in the world today that young people could get into, that ain't no use to them.
MR DEAN:	Oh, your boys and girls are fine young people. In fact, the people here are some of the most upstanding people I have met.
MRS COX:	Thank you! Mr Dean. Only thing ... well ...
MR DEAN:	Yes?
MRS COX:	Well, I don't know how else to put it, but, you know how people talk in these parts.
MR DEAN:	I assure you, Mrs Cox, that they will talk. I assume you mean Rosie's appointment. There is absolutely, nothing personal in the appointment, as they will know. Of course, Rose is my friend, and good friend too, but if I didn't think she was right for the job I wouldn't have wanted her for a replacement teacher.
MRS COX:	I don't say *I* feel that, that way; but people here ... you know how it is.
MR DEAN:	I understand. I'll have to bring it up at the next school board meeting. Then if there are very strong objections, I'll take appropriate action. You and Mr Cox'll come along, I hope.
MRS COX:	We'll be there. [*She has finished shelling the peas.*] Now, I have a question to ask you. I know you are busy and all that, but I wonder if you could help us with the church skit for the Easter Holidays. You know, just help the children to do their parts right? That is, if you have time.
MR DEAN:	[*thinking*] Sure, certainly, Mrs Cox. Did you like our last play?
MRS COX:	I enjoyed it very much. I laughed till I almost cried.
MR DEAN:	[*chuckles*] Yes, it was quite funny.
MRS COX:	[*rising with 'fanner' and bag of shells*] Excuse me, Mr Dean. I going to put this in the kitchen. I'll be right back.
MR DEAN:	Yes ...

[*As she exits, MR DEAN sits up, stretches, glances slyly at a clock on the wall. He passes his hand thoughtfully over his chin.*

ROSE approaches from left. She is a very handsome girl, with a kindly and slightly defeated air. She hesitates,

	in surprise at seeing MR DEAN sitting there. MR DEAN is instantly all attention, but manages to affect an air of relaxation and ease. ROSE is carrying what seems to be a parcel under one arm.]
ROSE:	Don't mind me, Mr . . . Bill. I just hadn't expected you, that's all. Let me put this package over here. [*ROSE puts package on side table*] Did you come to see Daddy?
MR DEAN:	No.
	[*ROSE returns from table.*]
MR DEAN:	May I offer you a seat, my dear. [*Beckons toward sofa.*]
ROSE:	Thank you, Mr . . . Bill. [*Sits.*]
MR DEAN:	Do you find it difficult to call me by my name? I'm just plain old Bill.
ROSE:	No, not really. I just think of you as Mr Dean, I guess.
MR DEAN:	Oh, that's all right dear. What have you been up to?
ROSE:	Well, nothing, you'd be bored anyway.
MR DEAN:	I promise you I won't.
ROSE:	I went out to get some cloth for Mother.
MR DEAN:	Yes, and what did you do on the weekend, while I was in Nassau?
ROSE:	Not much, I guess. Help Mother, go to church, sleep. Not very exciting I guess.
MR DEAN:	Did you have a good time at church?
ROSE:	Oh, come off it, Bill. You don't go to church to have a good time.
MR DEAN:	Well, you're right, you know.
ROSE:	And how was your trip? Did you accomplish what you set out to?
MR DEAN:	Partly. Partly not.
ROSE:	[*noticing the empty glass*] Can I get another drink?
MR DEAN:	Don't bother with that. Let's just sit and talk.
ROSE:	[*mischievously*] Yes, Sir.
MR DEAN:	Yes, Sir. Sweet Sir.
ROSE:	What will we talk about?
	[*MR DEAN gets up, stretches comically, attempts to touch his toes and does so. Straightens.*]
MR DEAN:	I know when I could touch my toes against a wall. Phew! [*Looks at ROSE*] Conflict of interest.
ROSE:	Conflict of interest? What have I done to cause conflict of interest?

MR DEAN:	[*standing*] It's not what you have done, love. It's what you are going to do.
ROSE:	And what am I going to do?
MR DEAN:	Good question. Deserves a good answer. Teach.
ROSE:	Teach? Me? When? Who said so?
MR DEAN:	One question at a time, sweet, one at a time. You'd make a very questioning wife.
ROSE:	A very questionable wife.
MR DEAN:	A very questioning wife.
ROSE:	I see. Who'll I teach?
MR DEAN:	One of my classes, I hope. Rose, you'll not have any objections, I hope.
ROSE:	Well, this is sudden . . . I'll see.
MR DEAN:	I have spoken to your mother. She hasn't quite said yes yet.
ROSE:	Yes.
MR DEAN:	Well, do you think you'd like to.
ROSE:	Er . . . , I don't know. It'll be a challenge for me. I'll have to think about it, I guess.
MR DEAN:	That's the girl. [*Goes over, tries to kiss her hand.*]
ROSE:	[*extracting her hand from his grasp*] . . . Bill! Suppose someone came in.
MR DEAN:	[*returns to his former seat. In a doleful voice*] Now, the conflict of interest.
ROSE:	Yes.
MR DEAN:	Well, you know, we have been seeing each other for some time.
ROSE:	Yes, though I still can't help calling you Mr Dean.
MR DEAN:	And you know that I have shown and expressed an inordinate fondness for you.
ROSE:	[*as if she is venturing into dangerous waters*] You . . . like er, you like me, you mean.
MR DEAN:	Rose, [*Draws closer to her*] Rose, I . . . I can't think of anyone else but you. I think of you all the time. Rose, I . . . I love you Rose. I want to ask you to marry me . . . Rose, will you marry me? [*All of this seems somewhat out of character for ROSE'S concept of what he is. She says nothing, perhaps she is dumbfounded. She is very nervous, certainly.*]
ROSE:	M – Me? Mr . . . er . . . Mother is coming. [*There is a sound stage left.*]
MR DEAN:	Rose, I am asking you to marry me.
ROSE:	Yeah . . . Uh . . . huh I mean, I hear you, Mr Dean.

	Oh, Mr Dean. [*She leans against him*] I . . . I don't know what to say . . . I . . .
MR DEAN:	[*tender*] My love. I shall ask your father.
	[*DANNY enters from left with an apologetic air. He is dressed in an oversized coat, a pair of pants that are a little too short, and a yellow shirt. He appears as if he has worked hard to appear in some of his best clothes. He is also carrying a large, longish parcel in one hand. He sees the couple on the sofa who move apart to appear more dignified. DANNY stops as if unwilling to enter further into the room and quietly turns as if he is ready to leave. ROSE moves as if to stop him, this relaxes him.*]
ROSE:	Danny!
	[*DANNY stops, but does not turn to face her.*]
	You're all dressed up this evening. Danny, who did you come to? Mother? [*Shouts*] Mother!
	[*MRS COX appears.*]
ROSE:	Danny brought something, I believe.
	[*DANNY turns to face them, sadly.*]
MRS COX:	Oh, Danny! How you doing, son? What you got there?
	[*DANNY says nothing.*]
MRS COX:	[*to MR DEAN*] Excuse Danny, he can't talk. [*To DANNY*] What you got there? Who's it for? [*Goes over to DANNY as if to accept package from him*] What it is? Fish? [*DANNY neither moves nor acknowledges that he has understood MRS COX. She reaches her hand toward him to take the package. He shakes his head to say no. He looks at ROSE, then at the package.*]
ROSE:	Who is it for, Danny? Daddy?
	[*DANNY responds by stretching his empty hand toward her. She is shattered and just sits there.*]
MRS COX:	Take it, Rose. Mr Knowles must be sent some fish.
	[*ROSE rises, extends her hand to take it. DANNY does not give it to her but beckons her closer.*]
ROSE:	What you got there?
	[*DANNY opens the package and shows ROSE the fish. He grins as he shows them.*]
ROSE:	Boy, these are nice fish. You all went fishing today, eh? Mother, come look at the fish.
	[*MRS COX approaches apprehensively and the two women examine the fish. MR DEAN rises, comes over to do likewise. DANNY turns his back to him, so as to*

144

	obstruct his view. Neither of the women seem to notice or attach much importance to his actions. DANNY pats ROSE on the back, gives her the fish.]
MRS COX:	Go put them in the kitchen, Rose. Excuse us please, Mr Dean.
	[*DANNY watches the two women exit.*]
MR DEAN:	[*who has resumed his seat*] Danny, my friend, how are you today?
	[*DANNY barely acknowledges him. ROSE returns, sits by MR DEAN who appears a little more relaxed.*]
MR DEAN:	Danny doesn't seem to want to talk to me today. [*Smiles*] Remind me to make Danny an usher when we get married . . .
ROSE:	[*makes an effort to shush him*] Danny is okay. He's just like that sometimes.
MR DEAN:	Danny must have that young girl on his mind. Eh, Danny? What's her name again? [*He is smiling good-naturedly but ROSE sinks back in her chair.*] I tell you, Danny, a woman is a weighty matter. A weighty matter.
	[*DANNY turns angrily toward him. His features soften and he turns to face the audience. He is very downcast; and it is obvious that he is crying. ROSE sits up to watch him. He slowly extracts something from his left-hand coat pocket. It is wrapped in white paper. He throws it away stage right without turning, then turns left and begins to walk off. He wipes his eyes with coat sleeve. MRS COX is seen standing at left.*]
ROSE:	Danny, is something wrong?
	[*At the sound of her voice, DANNY'S knees actually buckle, he actually staggers, as if he is about to fall. MRS COX rushes across stage as if to attempt to assist him; however, DANNY pushes her away without turning, and stumbles off, left. The three stare at his retreating back. ROSE is standing also. Silence falls and the lights die softly.*]

Scene 4

Living and dining area of SAM'S house. SAM is seated at wooden table, eating vigorously and somewhat boorishly.

Older woman of Scene 1 enters in apron and workdress, head wrapped in a scarf.

She walks toward SAM, pauses by table, wiping her hands on her apron. She is SAM'S mother. MRS RACHAEL KNOWLES.

MRS KNOWLES: Well ... that fish had enough salt to taste. Cos' I does lose my taste, you know; I gotta watch everything I eat, like the doctor say ...

SAM: [*as if she is interrupting his eating*] Uh? Uh? Oh; yeah, it taste awright. [*Drinks gluttonously and belches.*]

MRS KNOWLES: [*Sits down at table on empty downstage chair. Her manner is fidgety, as if something is on her mind*] Sam, I worried ...

SAM: [*picking teeth with fingernail*] Eh? What happen? What happen again?

MRS KNOWLES: I know you don't want to hear about it again, but I worried 'bout Danny.

SAM: [*leaning back*] Danny? Danny? You better worry about yourself. You done half-sick now.

MRS KNOWLES: Yes, but Sam, I can't help worrying about Danny. This is second day he been gone now. I don't know, I just feel something wrong. I had a bad dream and I don't know the meaning of it. I just feel something might a' happened.

SAM: Dream! Look like all you all does do is dream. I don tell you Danny big enough to find heself home when dark come, without people havin' to worry their head behind him. When he get hungry enough, you'll see him.

MRS KNOWLES: Yes, but ... ain't that what I talkin' about, is something else ... I been watching that boy for the past couple of months – it's like something building up inside him – sometimes I feel so sorry for him.

SAM: You always feeling sorry for that boy. And you better quit talkin' up for him. How you expect him to make it if anything was to happen to me?

MRS KNOWLES: Yes, but Danny ain't no fool, you know, only thing he can't do is talk. That boy just as bright as Jimmy or Carl. But you can't see that. I believe if he had someone to take the time with him ...

SAM: Well, you better take the time, I got my work to do.

MRS KNOWLES: Well, if you have your work to do, go ahead then. Don't let me stop you. I just telling you because one of these days I'll be dead and gone and might not be no one around to say nothing ...

SAM:	[*interrupts*] Yeah, but this ain't the first time that boy sleep out. And it look like it ain't going to be the last time, either.
MRS KNOWLES:	Yeah, but that's when you did hit him with that piece o' wood. Sam, you is my child but it does hurt my head to see you do your own child that way. You know where I find that boy that time? Guess? [*SAM stares at her blankly, sucking at his molars. She continues*] I meet that boy sitting on the top o' that high rock by Bobby Point looking out at the ocean, as if he wasn't going anyway any more. I had to plead with him to get him back. Lord, don't let me have to go through with that again ...
SAM:	You watch see if he don't turn up by sunset this evening.
MRS KNOWLES:	You and him ain't had no more fuss while you all was in the field?
SAM:	[*as if trying to hide his feeling, speaks gruffly*] No.
MRS KNOWLES:	You're sure?
SAM:	Must be them couple o' cuts I hit him with my belt.
MRS KNOWLES:	What he do?
SAM:	You should see how that boy was wasting my corn seed. Just like a person what never plant corn in his life.
MRS KNOWLES:	Yeah, well, all of that helps.
SAM:	What you mean by that?
MRS KNOWLES:	Yeah well, you is a man. Is many things you'll never understand.
SAM:	I don't know what you getting at.
MRS KNOWLES:	I don't know myself; I'll soon find out. Sam?
SAM:	Yeah.
MRS KNOWLES:	Sam promise me one thing, Sam. If Danny don't come home by dark tonight, you and Carl and Jimmy go look see if he might be somewhere not far.
SAM:	Not m ... okay. Okay. [*Resigns wearily.*]
MRS KNOWLES:	Maybe he ain't gone nowhere far. But myself I feel kind o' scared for that boy. He does take things so deep ...
	[*SAM sucks at teeth loudly. MRS KNOWLES rises to go about cleaning the table. Exits right. SAM leans back in chair, clears throat and belches. MRS KNOWLES returns with articles for putting table in order. SAM rises.*]

147

SAM:	I goin' back see if I could do something fo' sun go down. [*Begins exit.*]
MRS KNOWLES:	[*rearranging the cheap tablecloth*] Don't forget what I ask, now Sam.
SAM:	Yeah, clean that lantern and put oil in it, 'till I come back. [*Exits.*]
	[*MRS KNOWLES watches him go, stretches her back in the way of a painful old person, then continues her tidying. She begins to hum a mournful and familiar church tune. There is a light knock at right, the unexpectedness of which causes MRS KNOWLES to react with a slight start. She pauses, rigid, to await its repetition. There is a second knock. MRS KNOWLES turns toward left, rag in hand.*]
MRS KNOWLES:	Yes? Who that?
FEMALE VOICE:	It's me.
MRS KNOWLES:	[*to herself*] Me? [*To voice*] Come in, come in.
	[*ROSE enters hesitantly. She is dressed differently and seems a less serious person than in dream sequence of Scene 2.*]
ROSE:	Good evening, Mrs Rachael.
MRS KNOWLES:	[*warmly*] Rose! Well, come in child. I ain't see you in a long time. My, you're looking good. Come, child, sit down. I just tidying up a bit, here.
ROSE:	[*ROSE sits*] Thank you, ma'am.
MRS KNOWLES:	Yeah, I was just thinking to myself, you know, I dunno when last I see Rose. I figure you must have gone off for a couple o' days . . . well, how things with you, dear. How 'Saida doing?
ROSE:	Mamma? She doing all right . . .
MRS KNOWLES:	Her back ain't bothering her no more, eh?
ROSE:	No ma'am. She's okay now . . .
MRS KNOWLES:	So what's new with you, Rose? [*Sits in a chair*] I been hearing things, dear.
ROSE:	Well, I hope . . .
MRS KNOWLES:	No. Don't get me wrong now. Nothing out o' the way I heard. Only good things I heard.
ROSE:	Yes?
MRS KNOWLES:	I hear the date might soon fix.
ROSE:	[*shyly and nervously*] Well, I don't know, Mrs Rachael, I'll have to wait and see, I guess . . .
MRS KNOWLES:	Ain't nothing to be afraid of; though these days . . .

anyhow, my dear, I real glad for you. That Bill is a fine young man ... you all young people got the world ahead o' you. Is one o' the finest things any parents could wish for, to see their children grow up right and find someone nice when the time comes ...

ROSE: I hope so, too, Mrs Rachael.

MRS KNOWLES: Yes, dear. When you got a good man, it makes you feel like you have something worthwhile to live for ... Poor me, I lost mine long time ago. When you wasn't thinkin' about this side yet. Over and over I had the chance to get married again, but in the end seem like ain't none o' them could fill he shoes ... So ... Anything in particular ...?

ROSE: [ROSE smiles shyly] No, well, er, Danny dropped something when he came by to bring the fish. So I thought to bring it back for him ...

MRS KNOWLES: [interested] Danny? When Danny brought fish?

ROSE: That was Tuesday.

MRS KNOWLES: Tuesday. That was two days ago. I know Danny and Carl and Sam been fishing, but I didn't even know he was by you all.

ROSE: Yes, ma'am, he brought a couple of good fish.

MRS KNOWLES: Yes. I didn't know how much fish Sam caught but I mentioned that he ought to send 'Saida a meal.

ROSE: He brought the fish for me.

MRS KNOWLES: For you ... well, that's different, then.

ROSE: And me and mamma and Bill was there. And he didn't want to give it to nobody else. Bill cracked a little joke with him about his girl friend. He looked like he wasn't too pleased about something. Then Bill made the remark that he would get Danny to stand in our wedding when we get married. Then Danny got mad and threw something out of his pocket on the ground. And walked out.

MRS KNOWLES: And walked out?

ROSE: Yes, ma'am.

MRS KNOWLES: Hmmn. That ain't Danny. Something must have really ... well ... Don't laugh, Rose, when I say this, but think that boy must like you. That's all I could figure. Maybe he couldn't take ... And you all ain't seen him since?

ROSE: No, ma'am.

MRS KNOWLES:	Lord, child, you can't mind Danny. He head ain't good.
ROSE:	Yes, ma'am.
MRS KNOWLES:	Well, I'll tell you Rose, my dear. Danny been gone since Tuesday evening.
ROSE:	You mean he didn't come home?
MRS KNOWLES:	We ain't seen him. But since he did it before, I figure he'd come back yesterday or today. Me, I can't worry myself too much.
ROSE:	You think he might have gone up to Mrs Butler.
MRS KNOWLES:	I don't know, child. I doubt it. I was just telling Sam we got to go look see if we could find him when he come in this evening. All night last night and today I was worried in my mind. He such a serious child. And he can't talk to let you know what on he mind.
ROSE:	I hope nothing happened to him. He so . . . nice.
MRS KNOWLES:	Well, things like these happen for experience. I feel he might come back anytime now. Anyhow, child, I promise you this, whenever I see him again I going to talk to him. He shouldn't even be studying things like that, if that's what it is. You don't worry, I'll handle it.
ROSE:	[producing ring from handbag or pocket] Danny brought this ring when he brought the fish. I thought I should bring it back. [Gives it to MRS KNOWLES] I am sorry about all the trouble I cause.
MRS KNOWLES:	Don't worry about that now, that ain't nothing to concern yourself over. Danny is a man, and he should know better, anyhow. Forget Danny's foolishness. [Fingering ring] This ring looks familiar.
ROSE:	[rising] I guess you can tell him, too, that he's welcome to come to our house, anytime; when you see him.
MRS KNOWLES:	Sure dear. I ain't go let him cause no trouble with you all. But you know, Danny must be under the moon! Lord!
ROSE:	Mrs Rachael, I'm going now. I'll tell Daddy so he can go with you all to look. And I'll check back again, in case he comes. [Moves to exit.]
MRS KNOWLES:	Yes, child, thanks for calling. Tell all hello for me. [Rises to show ROSE to exit.]
ROSE:	Okay, Mrs Rachael. [Exits.]

MRS KNOWLES: [pauses a moment, centre, as if in thought] Well, that's something! Who would ha' thought it o' Danny! Poor thing, Lord, I hope he ain't gone do nothing foolish. I better go talk to Myrtle hear what she have to say. She being Danny's godmother, she might tell me something. She does know everything. Let me go now, before Sam comes.

[Music comes up, curtains close on her thoughts.]

Scene 5

Miss Myrtle's house. The evening of the same day. In the way that ancient two-roomed dwellings (of a sort rapidly becoming no longer known both in Nassau and in the Family Islands) are divided into sleep and living, we now see the living area of MISS MYRTLE'S. She is an ancient, wizened woman with a worn-looking stick and dressed in a fashion consistent with her age, locale and failing health. Her actions are those of a frail old woman who seems out of touch with reality, but there is a haunting sense of prophetic doom about her. She moves rarely and when she does so it is not in the manner of one whose actions may in any way be construed as being comic, but as one with a powerful sense of mission. The most startling feature about her is her voice, which ranges from a cracking, eccentric falsetto, when talking to her cats or her absent children, to almost masculine reverberations when imitating or asking one to enter. She is likely to be a frightening figure to the locals, who may not always understand the machinations of superstitions and other obscure crafts upon which her reputation is built.

The room may be set in grey with obscure lighting. The furniture and props should be of dull colours which tend to heighten the effect of terror in the room. Pictures on the wall are old and hung crookedly. Two or three of them are of persons deceased. There is a general air of disuse about the room, as if the spiders alone lived there, and the dust.

MISS MYRTLE is seated at right centre in a creaky rocking chair, her stick across her knees. At her close left on the floor is a large cat of indeterminate sex and origins, sleeping. As a last resort - since cats are a wilful breed and cannot be coerced into acting except by coaxful means, acting being too condescending an art for the same - a stuffed cat may be used. However, the stuffed cat must be in all cases handled in the manner accorded to the genuine article. MISS MYRTLE sits rocking.

The old woman pokes the area at right of her chair with her stick, as if feeling.

MISS MYRTLE: [in cracked old voice] Trouble! Trouble! Ooh Trouble! By Satan, I wonder where that cat is! I wonder where that cat is, heh, heh, heh. [Replaces stick on lap. Looks on left side of chair where cat is sleeping.] Trouble!

[*Lifts cat to her lap, strokes it*] For a cat with name like 'Trouble', you know you're sure lazy. Wouldn't even kill a cockroach. Kill a cockroach. And another thing, Trouble, you sleep out last night. Been chasing girls, eh. Trouble, you know what wrong with you? You getting too fat! If you get any fatter, I am going to have to skin you. [*Strokes cat hard*] Skin you and eat you. [*Cat attempts to move*] Easy, easy, baby, I didn't mean that. [*Soothes cat, who attempts to move*] Now, take it easy, boy. Don't go nowhere. There's only you and me and the sperrits here. Hee, hee, hee. You know that time when you scratched my han' and run away too? An' my twins, Jan and Dan, scared the hell outta you? Don't go outside. That's all I can tell you. Don't go outside.
Walter was out last night!
You don't believe me, eh boy
That's right
My own sweet Walter was out last night
[*Crosses her old hands across her bosom, no longer rocking. Her voice becomes tender.*]
My own sweet Walter was walking last night.
[*Returns to stroking cat*]
But you all cats don't believe anything. That's right.
[*Rocks*]
Last night
When the stars were dead
I lay with my head
At the foot of my bed
Waiting
Waiting for Walter to come
Through the western winder
I heard dem talking.
Even my twins
What gone in '22
Was calling for me
(and waitin' for you)
Hee, hee, hee.
Myrtle, Myrtle, they was sayin;
Mamma, Mamma.
Oh, they voices was so sweet
[*Voice rises, shrill*]
Why did they have to go?

Why did they all have to go?
Leaving me here with a crazy cat with thirteen
lives and not one life worth a durned cent.
You know, Trouble,
It's hard,
To put their supper out
And they don't come to eat it
And the food turning blue.
The trouble with you, Trouble
Is you don't really care,
The less they eat
The more you eat
An' you done eat too much a'ready.
How many times
Me one been down to the cemetery
To talk to them after dark
Tell me that.
They wouldn't hardly come here
And when they do come
They ready to run the first thing they hear.
[Calls]
Dan! An' Jan!
You all don't worry, honey
I soon come!
I soon come!
To keep you all company.
Won't be long!
[Sits up rigidly, turns head slowly to the left, smiles, folds
hands across bosom, begins to laugh.]
You hear them?
You hear what they say, Trouble.
They say: Yes, Mamma. Yes, Ma'am.
O, my sweet children.
Won't be long
Won't be long me and you all and Walter will be
walking and talking together.
[Pauses, then confidentially, but in deep voice, to cat]
And Trouble, too.
[Cat attempts to run away.]
Now, now I didn't mean that
Who'd want to carry a lazy old cat.
I come with nothing
And I going with nothing

'Cause I don't have nothing.
My only living boy, he in America long time.
My only living girl, she down in the city
years ago.
My grand, I seen them once
I need to see them so much.
Walter is under the ground,
My twins under the ground,
All my father's children
Under the ground.
When that moonlight speckles the floor through
them holes in the roof where the rain pours
then I know I is the last to live in this
dying ol' house, the last to sleep in this
lonely only house.
Go down, Trouble.
[*Puts down cat. Rocks*]
I wonder if he coming tonight
I wonder.
[*Rises heavily from chair, on stick*]
We uses to dance like this [*Mimics*]
When the two o' we was young.
We used to dance like this [*Steps*]
We was young and spunky then.
[*Calls*] Walter! [*Gestures toward picture*] Don't just
look down on me. Say something dear. Walter!
[*Pauses*] Oh, Lord, I better take myself in hand. I
does talk to myself too much. [*Shakes head sadly*]
People hear me, will think I gone crazy.
[*There is a light knock at the left entrance*]

MISS MYRTLE:	[*loudly*] Wait: ... oh ... [*In a dither to compose herself*] Yes? Who is there?
MRS KNOWLES:	It's me, Rachael.
MISS MYRTLE:	Oh. Come in child, come in. The door's open, I think.

[*MRS KNOWLES enters with a lit kerosene lantern.*]

MRS KNOWLES:	Good evening Miss Myrtle. How you doing?
MISS MYRTLE:	[*in an old voice, as if this is more to be expected of her by a visitor*] Can't complain too much, child, I still here. Sit down. [*Shows RACHAEL a chair, which RACHAEL accepts. She has returned to her own chair. RACHAEL turns down the lantern and sets it apart on a table.*]

MISS MYRTLE: Well, what it is, child. You look like you have a burden on your mind.

MRS KNOWLES: Is true, Miss Myrtle. It's Danny. He . . .

MISS MYRTLE: Your grandboy? Yeah, I know.

MRS KNOWLES: You know?

MISS MYRTLE: Yeah I sit here an' see him clear as day when he gone two days ago . . .

MRS KNOWLES: Miss Myrtle I don't know what to do, or where to turn. I come to you cos' I know you been such a help in the past. I ain't got no money now, but soon as I get something I go straighten you out.

MISS MYRTLE: Oh don't worry yourself with that, child. That's my godchild, you know. I responsible for him, too.

MRS KNOWLES: I bring a little tobacco. [*Produces tobacco in a small pouch from a bag and gives it to MISS MYRTLE, who accepts graciously, and puts it away.*]

MISS MYRTLE: Thank you, dear.

MRS KNOWLES: You think we'll be able to know something.

MISS MYRTLE: What if it's somethin' bad.

MRS KNOWLES: I just as soon know now.

MISS MYRTLE: You bring he picture?

MRS KNOWLES: Er . . . yes. [*Gives her DANNY'S picture.*]

MISS MYRTLE: [*passes dry hands over the picture*] Okay. You know what you can do. Get me them same candles from that safe over there and the matches. And put out your lantern.

[*MRS KNOWLES complies. The candles are placed in a circle on a table drawn centre. The stage is otherwise dark, or the light is very subdued. MRS KNOWLES sits downstage side of table, and MISS MYRTLE faces centre, a position to which she has hobbled on her crooked stick. The two women sit in an almost transfixed pose, as if their thoughts are the only things alive in the scene. Their voices will seem remote and otherworldly. There is very little movement. The candles are lit.*]

MISS MYRTLE: You touch one end o' the picture like how I do it and let's concentrate. Don't think of nothing else, but what happen. I'll ask you one o' two things, and you must answer the truth . . .

MRS KNOWLES: Yes.

MISS MYRTLE: When he gone?

MRS KNOWLES: Tuesday. Tuesday I miss him.

MISS MYRTLE: Where he gone?

MRS KNOWLES:	I don't know. I can't say.
MISS MYRTLE:	Why he gone?
MRS KNOWLES:	I don't rightly know.
MISS MYRTLE:	How old he is?
MRS KNOWLES:	Going on twenty-two.
MISS MYRTLE:	When he born.
MRS KNOWLES:	First fowl crow, twentieth o' April, 1938.
MISS MYRTLE:	A trouble child, a trouble child. [*Her voice becomes more hypnotic*] Into whose care are these, your nights and days entrusted?
MRS KNOWLES:	God.
MISS MYRTLE:	Into whose care are your unconscious hours entrusted? Give me an answer worthy of any experience.
MRS KNOWLES:	My dead grandmother, Ophelia Jones. You said she keeps an eye on me.
MISS MYRTLE:	You must believe, Rachael, that I am here. [*The voice changes in this*] I was there from the time you were a child.
MRS KNOWLES:	Yes ma'am.
MISS MYRTLE:	Rachael, what do you want me to do for Danny?
MRS KNOWLES:	See if you know where he is.
VOICES:	[*Shouts off-stage*] He is behind you, above you, in front of you!
MISS MYRTLE:	Don't mind them, they just trying to frighten you, they just evil. [*Raises voice*] Go away you all, in the name of goodness! [*Gestures angrily toward voices. The light blinks on and off.*]
MISS MYRTLE:	Just don't do what they say. Only look at the candles. Your grandboy got a guardian, too. Your brother, James.
MRS KNOWLES:	Yes. He had one short leg.
MISS MYRTLE:	You want to call him?
MRS KNOWLES:	Miss Myrtle, I ain't sure I can take it.
MISS MYRTLE:	None o' them can do you anything. The dead has no power.
MRS KNOWLES:	Yes, okay then.
MISS MYRTLE:	Stars are sometimes our fortuitous guides, Steering us past many a sinister fate. Stars hold their silent watch o'er all our doings. In the ether realm, between the living and nothingness.

156

Where stars unite with dying novas there float
forever rafts of departed luminaries.
In a twinkle and a closing of eyes
We become also
Fading stars
Echoes in a timeless space.
Hear the echoes.
Hear the echoes of all past generations.
I am the hearer of beginnings
And endings.
I am the Eve of echoes.
I shall call him whom you have loved well from
another world.
He shall come, he shall show empathy with your
exigency,
He shall answer
For you have loved each other well.
[*To MRS KNOWLES*]
Hold my hands. Now.
O
phel
ia!
Ophelia!
Ophelia Jones
Come.
I need you,
Rachael needs you,
Daniel needs you.
[*Woman's voice, deep and as from a distance*]

VOICE:	Who is it, that disturbs my sleep
	After fifty years?
	Who is it?
MISS MYRTLE:	It is me, Myrtle,
	William's daughter.
VOICE:	What is it you want?
MISS MYRTLE:	Rachael has lost Daniel.
	Where is Daniel?
	[*A woman in funeral dress enters partially from right*]
WOMAN:	That is what you woke me for?
	Let him be lost,
	I shall never get back to sleep.
MISS MYRTLE:	Where is Daniel?
WOMAN:	He is not with us. That's all I can say.

MISS MYRTLE:	Rachael, watch your diet careful, and take all the rest you can get.
WOMAN:	Myrtle, you never could carry a straight message. I going now.
MISS MYRTLE:	Where he is now?
WOMAN:	Ask James. I going now.
	Goodbye, Rachael, dear.
	And take care. [*she vanishes.*]
MISS MYRTLE:	James!
	James!
	Come! I need you.
	[*There is no response. There is a sudden sound of violent and ghostly laughter off right.*]
VOICE:	[*jumbled*] Listen to her, she want James. Which James you want Myrtle. Is a lot of James here. James the backslider, James Wilson, James who thief the cow, James the catechist. You want all o' we?
MISS MYRTLE:	I askin' and callin' James Grey. Rachael's brother.
VOICE:	Oh. You want short-leg-James.
MISS MYRTLE:	[*to RACHAEL*] Don't take no notice.
	[*To voices*] Go away, you evil things.
	James Grey!
MAN'S VOICE:	Yeah, Yeah. Who that is?
MISS MYRTLE:	Rachael and Myrtle!
	[*A man enters, attired in the funeral clothes of an early period. He remains at far right as he speaks. He has a limp.*]
MAN:	Rachael! Rachael! My sis! And Myrtle! Well, what the problem now?
MISS MYRTLE:	Danny gone. We ain't know where. Can you tell us?
MAN'S VOICE:	What do you see?
MISS MYRTLE:	I see footprints on the beach at Ambergris Head.
	I see a man like a bird walking into the lonely water
	I hear him call:
	Rose! I love
	I love!
	But it is of no purpose
	I see the waters close around him
	I hear his words ascend from the sea
	As the words of a dying child who is finally lost.
	I see the surf wipe away his going.
MRS KNOWLES:	[*screams*] My boy, my boy done drowned!

158

MISS MYRTLE: [*MISS MYRTLE lifts her head, she calms RACHAEL.*]
Wait!
I see a man like a dog
Toward the shore
In the shallow flats he stumbles
Out of the brown grass toward the sand
He falls
He is face down, silent
He is weeping
He is weeping and naked upon the sand
He sleeps
[*She rises, illustrates with her old arms and her crooked stick*]
The sun comes over Tom's Hill
He awakes
Under the trees he sleeps, awakes
He rises
Stumbling naked through the woods
His skin is torn
He stumbles all day through the woods
His skin is torn
He stumbles all day through the woods
He sits
His mouth creates her name
His hands create her face
His heart recreates her voice
She is in him
A great hurt which tears and bedazzles
Like the bright beak of an asprey
In a golden fish at dawn.
Her voice
Her face
Her hands
Her love
They deny!
Deny his being!
He is running toward the west
His voice runs as the voice of dying men
Stop him! O stop him!
He runs
I see something!
Stop him, James
He is falling

MRS KNOWLES:	[*shouting*] Stop it, Miss Myrtle, stop it!
MISS MYRTLE:	He is falling deep.
	O, his head!
	O, his arms!
	Into the mud, and brackish water and stones
	[*She is hypnotized and does not heed MRS KNOWLES.*]
	He whimpers [*MRS KNOWLES bursts into tears.*]
	He whimpers
	His breath weakens
	He is
	[*She stops trembling, where she stands, looking toward the right, covers her face in her hands.*]
	Thank you James
	Thank you James
	[*She goes over to RACHAEL*]
	Rachael, it's all right
	He will be all right
	But he is now very sick
	[*Gets lantern, hands it to RACHAEL*]
	Go now hear
	God go with you
	Be strong
	Go now, he might be dying
	[*She helps MRS KNOWLES to her feet. MRS KNOWLES exits. The lights come up. MISS MYRTLE returns to her chair, rocks wiping her eyes. The rocking becomes gradually furious, violent, the lights go down.*]

Scene 6

A field, which might be suggested by a suitable backdrop, an occasional tree. MR SAM KNOWLES is seated on the end of a low wall, suggestible by stonework painted on a box. He is wearing a straw hat, has a machete, and is wiping his face, as if he been sweating profusely. MRS RACHAEL KNOWLES is nearby, as if she has just been in conversation with him. Two other persons are on stage, one at deep left, one at right. The principals are near centre stage.

UPSTAGE MAN:	Danny! Oh Danny!
DOWNSTAGE WOMAN:	Danny!
SAM:	Well, I done look everywhere. I 'bout ready to give up.

MRS KNOWLES: Let's go on a little further. I just feel he ain't far away now.

SAM: Now, I most tired as a dog. And lazy as that boy is, he ain't come this far, no how. Two chance he ain't somewhere laughin' at us.
[*The two others go off left and right.*]

MRS KNOWLES: He might be somewhere, but I am sure he ain't laughin', by now. Might even be dead, for all we know.

SAM: You don't have to talk like that, Mama. [*Rises*] Come let's go. [*They move as if to go off, right. A cry stops them.*]

A VOICE: Come with the light, Willie, come quick!

MAN'S VOICE: You see something?

VOICE: Right here in this hole. I hear something. Hold the light, lemme see. O my God!

MAN: He ain't dead, eh?

VOICE: Sam! Everybody! Come! We find him! We find him! [*SAM and RACHAEL respond to the callers off-stage. There is a pause, while with appropriate off-stage conversation DANNY'S barely living body is brought up.*]

A MAN: [*entering right and shouting off right*] I going see if I could find the nurse! [*He hurries off left with his machete, and straw bag at his shoulder. Persons enter from right, including SAM and MRS KNOWLES. They bear DANNY among them, carefully, on a makeshift stretcher. The figure of DANNY is mudstained, bloodstained.*]

SAM: Put him down a minute, let me get a better hold.

SAM AND OTHER STRETCHER BEARERS: [*they put him down*] Phew!

MRS KNOWLES: You all gotta watch that head o' he own. We ain't know how bad he injure.

ANOTHER WOMAN: Is a wonder he didn't bleed to death down there.

MRS KNOWLES: Child, it's nothing but God. Bless God!

SAM: Come, you all, let's get him in the house. Everybody lift, one time.
[*They carry DANNY off, left, in the manner of a very heavy but fragile burden. The lights go down.*]

Scene 7

We return, as in a non-ordinary reality, to Scene 1. The little bedroom is arranged in the previous manner; except that everything looks much cleaner. The sleeper in the bed is again DANNY. This time he is swathed in bandages about the head and appears to wear a cast on one foot. He is partially covered by a sheet and is lying on his back. A woman, MRS KNOWLES, sits by his bed at a small table at left, on which there is a lamp. He groans from time to time, and MRS KNOWLES attends to his wants.

The MAN of ethereal dress and manner is at right of the bedroom scene and may be spotlighted during his speaking.

ROSE sits at the foot of the bed, her hands in her lap. She does nothing. Very faint music.

MAN:

There is in each of us a passion for a reality not of our familiarity; a passion which when enkindled by affection drives us to a place we come to sometimes between our deaths and birth. It is the most feared place of all, a place from which there is no deliverance, from which nothing in the past nor future knowledge can save us; we come into a clear place, where nothing is mysterious, where there is no magic; it is the place called Truth. There one's destiny is revealed; one encounters his most important enemy yet his most important friend; the sense of fate and sorrow.

Sorrow comes from an ennobling pity then, from a clarity that there is nothing which can be as the will would have it, everything follows its own rules, its own paths and thus is bound within these; we cannot teach, ·or even expect, the fishhawk to love the heron, though they both be fishing birds – nor do the white and black crab dwell in the same habitat, if left to their own devices; – nor can a beautiful child conceive, without some learned and thus artificial response, of an ugly child as beautiful in the physical sense though, be it as it may, children have a saving sense of innocence, a sense of inherent beauty.

Picture, then, a young man, whose sense of appreciation has been brought into bloom by the most ancient and consuming of purposes, which is love. Who is the young man and why should he eschew love? What seems a simple logistic problem, upon superficial and self-biased consideration does not readily resolve itself.

We sense, with overpowering and sometimes fatal instinct, ourselves as the centre of beings, the magnet to which all life must be drawn, in our extreme we think of ourselves as God. For since we cannot discover, by much thought or argument, our sense of immediate past nor our future, we are inclined to believe our coming a fortuitous, deic event which has no precedence, nor can its parallel be sensed in other beings of lesser powers around us.

If power were given in random and satisfying measure to all, there would be no sense of fate, for the sense of fate arises from the temporary absence or deprivation of power.

Here I give you a representation; we have known even in our short lives or the lives of others of such as these: An otherwise stable and resolved man or woman, sees a person from afar or close at hand – one whose form or voice or whose inherent qualities present them as being ultimately desirable as a friend, a lover, a husband, a wife, a mistress. The response elicited by this feeling is presumably, in most cases, subjugated to the sense of responsibility. I have my own, my own, my own, he or she says, but what if I only had that? The sense of fate coming before or after the decision to follow heart in this, in cases: He or she is altogether beautiful and satisfies my sensual awareness, my sense of total beauty, but I am not so, no, not to this being; I am only another one who merits a nodding of the head, a good morning.

MRS KNOWLES: Rose, you can go now if you wish. I believe he'll rest for the remainder of the night.

ROSE: I think I'll stay a little longer to keep you company. [*Danny groans softly.*]

MAN: Those who are separated from us and from whom we are divided as if by a strong transparent barrier, upon whom our lonely thoughts, whatever their nature, may linger – whose thoughts may linger upon ourselves; the lonely eye which follows us in streets and chance meetings or whom our eyes follow even after they depart – the waiting, the broken, the seemingly happy, the carnal, the crippled the rational, these are the makers of dreams.

Not the irrational who live outside themselves; we are all partial to the dream; we are all potato dreamers in some degree. Our dream built with members of chance reflection and lifelong jackdaw gathering, cries out for fulfilment. We may follow, if as moths to a flame or as trapped birds to a clear pane of glass, seeking the freedom it enticingly presents until we come to truth, a brutal, impartial judge whose only passion is order. He serves as the final sentinel at the door of fate, whose message is no, though he does not chain the door.

Through the door and beyond is life and death, none of which can be faintly adumbrated beforehand except by truth, the sentinel. Hope is the door, he says. It is safer on this side. Stay.

Those of us who have lived too long with a sense of fate and sorrow can scarce ignore the enchanting world beyond the door. We would hasten to our fate out of a sense of loss and urgency: You are being foolish.

Which of us has not screamed – I shall have this, or I should rather die. Which of us have not felt the courage to pursue love to its end, even death. Coming close to death we learn the truth. That truth is order, that order is beauty, that beauty shows no empathy.

DANNY: [*as if waking from a dream, shouts*] I don't love you any more, Rose! Go away!

[*Both women stare in surprise at hearing him speak.*]

DANNY: I don't need you no more. I can make it on my own.
MAN   Thus a man finds what is best after a traumatic descent into the depths of his being. Some of us [*Beckons half-heartedly toward ROSE*] act out of a sense of propriety and guilt, masking our true feelings behind niceties. Not that such a love as between these two could not exist, but it was hardly likely to be. She is a lover of dream princes, he is a lover of beauty near. It has taken much to convince him that his image of himself is tragic in that it is not that by which his peers remember him. In the love of beauty is the hope of his kind. Perhaps he shall be comfortable with shadows in the end, perhaps she

shall learn to love him out of good-heartedness, perhaps she shall kiss him goodbye and this will be his achievement. But because it has been made so real to him he shall love her; to the end of his days, perhaps, making himself 'comfortable with shadows'. There is no real hope for his love – none whatsoever. Do not feel too deeply for him, who has once stunned himself against the plate-glass window.

That which we would have is certainly the most cherishable, but that which we have is infinitely more valuable.

Therefore in the dream, let us take the sense of fate and sorrow with us and if in our long fantasy sleep we are carried far and wide through the open door, on awaking let us remember it only as a dream and these fond memories as the delectable fruits of sleep. [*The music rises, lights die softly.*]

END

Biographical Sketches

Ava Adams, executive secretary, was born in Nassau in 1952. She attended Government High School and later secretarial school in Boston. She loved reading and writing poetry and was motivated by the need to express herself and the desire to make a contribution to her society. She particularly enjoyed reading the works of American poet Nikki Giovanni and also local poets.

Cheryl Albury, public administrator, was born in Exuma in 1944. She attended Government High School. She pursued writing as a hobby, producing, at first, personal introspective poems. She attended the University of the West Indies and the University of Miami. She enjoys yoga, amateur acting, theatre and travel. She was influenced by several writers including Donne, Keats, Hopkins, Cohen and Angelo. Later, developments in the Bahamas motivated her to focus on social issues.

Norris Carroll, barrister-at-law, was born in Long Island in 1942. He attended the Bahamas Teachers' College, the University of Exeter and College of Law in London. Yielding to an urge to express anger and to create laughter, he wrote plays, poems, novels and songs. He published in the Anthology of Bahamian Poetry of the Bahamian Students' Association in London in 1972.

Jerome Cartwright, teacher, was born on Long Island in 1948. He attended Government High School and later studied at the Bahamas Teachers' College and the University of the West Indies. His urgent desire to express what he felt about 'the whole spectrum of man's emotions as conditioned by all elements of his environment', led him to write. He has also written and directed short plays.

Meta Davis Cumberbatch, 1900–1978. Born in Trinidad, she was educated there and in London. Later she graduated from the Royal Academy of Music, London, with the Diploma of the London Royal Academy of Music. She pursued a career as a concert pianist in London, New York and other cities of North America and in the West Indies. Shortly after her move to the Bahamas she became ill and it was during this time that she began to write seriously. Her poems were often broadcast and were published locally and internationally. She published an anthology in 1960. Later she wrote and produced plays, choreographed ballets and folklore productions. She established the Nassau Festival of Arts and Crafts which played a vital role in promoting the Arts in the Bahamas.

In recognition of her contribution to the Arts she was awarded the Distinguished Citizens Award and later became a Member of the British Empire during the visit of the Queen to the Bahamas.

Eugene Dupuch, 1912–1981. He attended Queen's College and later St John's University of Toronto and Lincoln's Inn, London. Among his numerous activities he was a member of the House of Assembly from 1950–1967 and was a senator in 1967. He was also a Judge of the Supreme Court in 1976. He served in many capacities in several legal bodies including President of the Bar Association and Chairman of the Bar Council. He was granted the right to retain his title 'Honourable' by the Queen, in recognition of his services on the old Colonial Executive Council. In 1956 he was granted the C.B.E. He was also a professional journalist and wrote a series of reports of the celebrated trial for the murder of Sir Harry Oakes. His *Smokey Joe Says*, written weekly in 1936, were very popular and are still greatly enjoyed by everyone.

Cleveland Eneas, dentist, was born in Nassau in 1915. He attended Government High School and later graduated from Tuskegee Institute and Meharry Medical College. His interests are many and varied and, in addition to writing, include music, philosophy, politics, reading, teaching theology and religion. His work has been influenced by Tennyson, Robert Browning, and Thursman. He is particularly interested in history, especially local events that have shaped the history of his people. He knows quite a bit about it and wants to preserve it for the future. This has prompted him to publish his well-known book, *Bain Town*.

Phylmos Hall was born in Nassau in 1942. He attended Southern Senior School and St Augustine's College. He has been trained in many areas, but spends most of his time writing. He has always felt an urge to explain real life events and experiences through fiction and has been writing since 1964. He was inspired by the work of Jeanne Thompson and P. Anthony White. He loves reading and also enjoys acting, singing and music. His poem *Changing* was published locally. He received a National Festival of Arts award for short story writing in 1977. His real talent lies in the writing of short stories and plays.

Eunice Humblestone, bank manager and interior designer, was born in Nassau in 1935. She attended Government High School and studied Business

Administration privately. She studied Interior Design and languages in London. Among several organisations of which she is a member are the Nassau Music Society, Alliance Française and the Dundas Centre for the Performing Arts. She has travelled widely through Europe, the Far East, the West Indies and the three Americas. An avid reader from childhood, she writes merely for relaxation.

Robert Johnson, Consultant in Public Relations and Advertising, was born in Nassau in 1948. He was educated at Government High School. During 1964–1965 he was a columnist for the *Bahamian Times*. Later, he studied at the University of the West Indies, where he was a regular contributor to campus publications. He worked for some time in the field of Public Relations and later became a lecturer and then Community Relations Officer at the College of the Bahamas. In this capacity he was responsible for several campus publications. He started and co-ordinated the present Anthology Committee until his move to Freeport, but is still an associate member of the committee. He enjoys painting, playing the guitar and writing. His anthology, *The Road*, has been used in Bahamian Schools.

Dennis Knowles, 1948–1980, was born in Nassau. He attended Queen's College in Ealing, Middlesex, England. He was an artist and worked with music, poetry and did string art. As a musician he did some singing in shows with Pat Rahming. He was influenced in his work by Pat Rahming and Paul Riley.

Ileana Mcdermott, writer, was born in Nassau in 1936. She attended Queen's College and later McGill University. She is a voracious reader and enjoys writing both prose and poetry. She has published a column called *Scattered Thoughts* in the *Nassau Guardian*. Her desire is 'to bring about improvements and reform in the Bahamas'. She has enjoyed reading Hemmingway, Lawrence, van der Post and Shakespeare and her writing reflects their combined influence.

Don Major was born in Nassau in 1950. After completing high school he attended Lakewood College, Alabama, where he studied English and Business Administration. Later he completed first year Law at Ohio State University. He has also done a writing course with Barett School of Journalism in Chicago. He has been trained in voice, piano and other instruments and has studied several languages. He has worked as an accountant, a lecturer in English and Communications, a teacher and is now an administrator. Among his many interests are reading, writing, music, public speaking, travelling and drama. He has been influenced by the works of Tennyson, Wordsworth, Sandbury and Khalil Gibson and by Susan Wallace to use Bahamian dialect.

Livingston Malcolm, Methodist Minister, was born in Nassau. He attended public school and Queen's College. Later he studied for the Ministry at United Theological College of the West Indies. His interests are drama, music and writing poetry and plays. In this he has been motivated by the desire to provide guidelines which would shape the lives and minds of future generations. He has published two books, *Reminiscence in Poetry* (1977) and *A Taste of Salt* (1979).

Melissa Maura, artist, was born in Nassau in 1956. She attended St Andrews School and Oriel School in England. Later she studied at Heatherly School of Fine Art, London. She is particularly interested in writing and illustrating fantasy stories for children and has been influenced by C.S. Lewis. An ardent supporter of and worker for the conservation of wildlife, she has written short weekly articles with drawings of endangered animals for *The Tribune*.

Percival Miller, civil engineer, was born in Long Island. He attended Government High School and later the University of the West Indies and Southern University, Louisiana. He is particularly interested in philosophy, music, reading and writing and has published an anthology and poems in other journals including the literary journal of the University of Kentucky. He has been inspired by the West Indian writers, Harris, Hearne and V.S. Naipaul.

Edward Minnis, artist, was born in Nassau in 1947. He studied at St John's College, Government High School and later at McGill University. His main interest after painting has been song writing and his songs reflect his 'fascination with the life and customs of Bahamian people'. He has produced several albums which are very popular locally.

Liam Nelson, lecturer in art, was born in Nassau in 1931. He is a graduate of Methodist College, Queen's University and Stranmillis College in Belfast, Ireland. Later he attended London University. He writes purely for enjoyment and has felt an affinity for the works of Eliot, Cummings and Yeats. He enjoys 'creative thinking in relation to art, poetry and literature'.

Van and Gerry Oldham are a husband and wife team and both teachers. Van Oldham was born in Eleuthera in 1944. Gerry Oldham was born in Crewe, England, in 1933. They both hold the L.C.P. and M.Sc. degrees. They have enjoyed writing plays, poems and songs, many of which have been used in the Music and Drama Festivals and for which they have won several awards.

In an attempt to share their work with their colleagues they published the anthology, *Inside-out*, which has become popular in schools in the Commonwealth of the Bahamas.

Melvin Rahming, college lecturer, was born in Nassau in 1943. He attended St Augustine's College and the Bahamas Teachers' College. He studied further at Oklahoma Baptist University and the University of Oklahoma. His work has been influenced by Donne, Eliot, Imamu Baraka and other writers. His writing is an attempt 'to preserve the authenticity of his life's moments and to articulate the common source of all human experience'. He has published *Silence and Symphony* and *Racial Somnolence in the West Indian Novel*. Other interests are music, drama, literature of all kinds and athletics.

Patrick Rahming, architect, was born in Nassau in 1944. He attended Government High School and later McGill University. He is a versatile artist who, as a singer, has produced albums and won an award. As an actor he is a member of the Bahama Drama Circle and has performed in several productions. He is a keen sportman. His artistic work springs from his 'concern for the disintegration of the human community, the lack of continuity in Bahamian traditions and political frustration'. He has been inspired by Dylan, Sparrow, Adamson, Leroi Jones, Jenks and Melvin Rahming and has published an anthology, *Reflections*.

Ashley Saunders, teacher, was born on Bimini in 1945. He attended the American School. Later he studied at the University of Wisconsin and Harvard University. As an actor/producer, he performed in and co-produced movies for Jajuar Films, Venezuela. As a song-writer and poet he has published several volumes including *Voyage into the Sunset* (1976), *The Sun Makes It Red* (1977), *The Night of the Lionhead* (1979) and *Searching for Atlantis* (1980).

Antoinette Smith, teacher, was born on New Providence. She attended Government High School. Her general interests are trade unionism and politics. She enjoys writing poetry and short stories. Her work has been influenced by V.S. Naipaul, Graham Greene and Roger Mais.

Colin Tatem, journalist and business manager, was born in the Turks and Caicos Islands in 1942. He was educated at St John's College. He is a Fellow of the British Society of Commerce and of the Association of Business Managers and Administrators, U.K. As a writer, he is a member of the Institute of Journalists (U.K.) and The American Society of Writers. He wrote his first story at age eleven and has never stopped writing since. He has produced hundreds of short stories, columns on the Caribbean and feature articles in *The Tribune*, *The Guardian* and *The Freeport News*. He has also acted and directed for the Bahama Drama Circle and the Freeport Players Guild. His life and work have been influenced by Kipling, Faulkner, Fitzgerald, Churchill, Buckly and Kissinger.

Marcella Taylor, college professor, was born on Long Island in 1933. She attended Xavier's Academy, the College of St Benedict, Minnesota, and the University of Iowa. She has enjoyed the works of Dickinson, Thomas, Levertou, Yeats, Plath and has had excellent teachers in Galway Kinnell, Kathleen Fraser, John Silkin, George Starbuck and Marvin Bell. She is a prolific writer and has published poems in numerous American journals including *Carleton Miscellany*, *Quest*, *Wisconsin Review* and *Wisconsin Quarterly*. She enjoys travelling, reviewing films and working with writers. She held a workshop for writers in this volume and has herself written the critical introduction of this anthology.

K. Andre Turnquist, legal clerk, was born in Nassau in 1957, and is a graduate of R.M. Bailey High School. He has always enjoyed reading and has been motivated to write as a means of self-expression and from a desire to criticise and alter the existing social structure. His writing is also a medium for discovering himself.

Mizpah Tertullien, senator and psychologist, was born on Ragged Island in 1929. She attended Government High School and, later, Lincoln School for Nurses in New York. She obtained both her degrees at the University of Ottawa, Canada. Among her many interests are legal, political and socio-cultural activities, handicrafts, reading and writing. She has published *Psychologically Speaking* and *Bahamiana Culturama: Old Stories and Riddles*. She also has a weekly newspaper column. Her work has been influencd by Caribbean writers including Reid, Naipaul, Henriques, Lamming and Carew, who encouraged her to write in her own Bahamian dialect.

Chester Thompson, real estate agent, was born on Elbow Cay. He attended Western Senior School and later the University of Toronto. His love of reading developed his 'creative urge to record the colourful history and mores of the islands through the medium of the short story'. His writing has been influenced by Bates and Steinbeck.

Telcine Turner-Rolle, college lecturer, writer, was born on New Providence in 1944. She attended Queen's College and Government High School. Later, she studied at U.W.I. and then was awarded a fellowship from Northwestern University. Her interest in drama led to her involvement in the Bahama Drama Circle where she became active in productions. She has always loved writing and won many prizes and awards during her school career. She writes to relieve feelings of anger and frustration at the state of things. Her play, *Woman Take Two*, has enjoyed tremendous success and her book of poetry, *Song of the Surreys*, has been very well received and much used in primary schools in the Bahamas.

Susan Wallace, educator and personnel manager, was born in Grand Bahama in 1931. She was educated at St John's College and the Bahamas Teachers' College. Later she studied at the University of Exeter and the University of Miami. Her activities are varied. She is the proprietor of a native craft shop, a dress designer, the musical director of a choir and a writer of poems, short stories and plays. She was 'moved to express the feeling that comes from a deep sensitivity to her environment'. She published the first anthology used in schools in the Bahamas which included poems in Bahamian dialect. Her books *The Bahamian Scene*, *Island Echoes* and *Back Home* are well-known to school children throughout the Bahamas.